BOOK 3

Spell It Out

READING/SPELLING WORKSHOP

D1360141

Globe Book Company, Inc.
Englewood Cliffs, New Jersey

BOOK 3

Spell It Out

READING/SPELLING WORKSHOP

Phillip K. Trocki

The Author

Phillip K. Trocki, author of *Spell It Out, Books 1, 2*, and *3*, and co-author of the *A Need to Read* series, received his bachelor's degree in English and secondary education from Boston State College. He has taught English and reading for the Los Angeles Unified School District, and has participated in the Writer's Program at the University of California at Los Angeles. For several years, Mr. Trocki was a staff member of the *New York Times*. He is currently assigned as a studio teacher in Los Angeles, and has most recently authored *Spelling Workout*, a six-volume spelling series for Modern Curriculum Press.

Editor: Janet Rosenthal

Photo Acknowledgments:

Pages 1, 2, 4, Burt Reynolds Productions, Inc.; 9, 10, 12, G. W. (Jerry) LaFavor, courtesy of Skytypers, Inc.; 17, National Park Service; 18, photography, Michael P. Johnson, equipment courtesy of Base Camp; 20, Mike Hoover; 25, U.S. Fish and Wildlife Service/J. Malcolm Greany; 26, U.S. Fish and Wildlife Service/Ralph Touen; 28, Ministry of Tourism Government of British Columbia; 41, Michael P. Johnson; 33, 34, 36, National High School Rodeo; 42, Rex Weyler; 44, 81, 89, 90, 92, 106, H. Armstrong Roberts; 49, 50, 52, Seaquest International, Inc.; 57, 58, 60, Barney Josephson; 65, 68, photography, Philip Galgiani, photographs courtesy of San Francisco Museum of Modern Art; 66, photographs, Mary McNally, photograph courtesy of San Francisco Museum of Modern Art; 73, 74, 76, Denis Brodeur; 82, 84, The University Museum, University of Pennsylvania; 97, 98, 100, Maren Seidler; 105, State of Maine Development Office; 108, Maine Department of Commerce and Industry; 113, 114, 116, The Boston Red Sox; 121, 124, Taurus Photos/E. Kroll; 122, Michael Halsband; 129, Allstate Life Insurance Company; 130, 132, Epilepsy Foundation of America; 137, 138, Franklin Williamson/Zoological Society of Philadelphia; 145, 148, Aerovironment, Inc.; 146, Miami-Metro Department of Publicity and Tourism; 153, 154, Smithsonian Institution; 156, Philadelphia Museum of Art.

Second Edition 1987

ISBN: 0-87065-338-5

Published simultaneously in Canada by Globe/Modern Curriculum Press.
Copyright © 1985 by Globe Book Company, Inc. 190 Sylvan Avenue, Englewood Cliffs, New Jersey 07632. All rights reserved. No part of this book may be kept in an information storage or retrieval system, transmitted or reproduced in any form or by any means without the prior written permission of the publisher.

PRINTED IN THE UNITED STATES OF AMERICA

4   5   6   7   8   9

To the Student

Spell It Out, Book 3 is designed to give you practice in reading and spelling. Both are skills you need to communicate with other people.

Each unit is divided into two parts. First, in Developing Reading Skills, you will find a short story about an interesting topic or personality. Some subjects you may already know about. Others may be totally new to you. In any case, read the story, paying attention to the details and the point the author is trying to make. Then answer the questions that follow without looking back to the story for help.

The second half of the unit deals with Developing Spelling Skills. The words you will be working with are ones that you use every day. In fact, many of the examples have been taken from the story that you just read. A few rules of spelling will be explained in the lessons. But, unfortunately, there are always exceptions to the rule. Some words will have to be memorized. Try to memorize them before you begin the exercises. That way, you will have more practice writing the words correctly. If you do spell a word wrong, don't be discouraged. Some words are harder to spell than others. Just try to find out what it is about the word that makes it hard to spell. Keep that in mind when writing the word again.

Above all, enjoy yourself when using this book—that's what learning is all about!

Contents

1 Buddy

Burt Reynolds really isn't the rough, tough guy seen in his movies. He's an actor, playing the part of a rough, tough guy. Instead of using his fists, in real life, Burt uses his talents to prove himself. He learned to depend on his talents back in junior high school.

Because he is part Native American and part Italian, some of his classmates made fun of him. They used to call him names like "mullet." That's a kind of fish. Burt came from a part of town where people caught fish for a living. But one day after he won a race, the name-calling stopped. Burt proved that he was the fastest runner in the whole school. Soon the kids began to call him "Buddy," a nickname they still call him back home in Florida.

For Burt, athletic talents opened the door to Florida State University. Football occupied most of his time. But during his second year, an injury forced him to give up the game and his education. Burt dropped out of college and began to work on his acting career.

"I've always been sorry I never finished college," says Burt. So he is now returning to his studies, part-time. He would like to complete his last two years of college. "Eventually," says Burt, "I'd like to go somewhere and teach high school for a semester or two."

A busy acting and directing career takes up all his time now. Also, there's work to be done on his horse ranch. Over a hundred horses, deer, and some cattle require a lot of time and effort. But Burt's folks do a good job of caring for things while he's away. No matter where he is, Burt calls them every weekend. "My parents mean everything to me," says Burt. Success hasn't spoiled Burt Reynolds. As he says, "I'm still Buddy."

● REVIEWING YOUR READING

Circle the letter beside the word or phrase that best completes the sentence.

1. Burt Reynolds is a professional

   a. teacher.
   b. actor.
   c. athlete.
   d. rancher.

2. Burt Reynolds is part

   a. Irish.
   b. Cuban.
   c. Native American.
   d. Russian.

3. Burt's classmates called him names until he won

   a. a race.
   b. a fight.
   c. an acting award.
   d. a spelling award.

4. According to the story, you can conclude that Burt grew up in

   a. California.
   b. Iowa.
   c. Florida.
   d. Georgia.

5. According to the story, you can conclude that Burt played football in

   a. grammar school.
   b. junior high.
   c. high school.
   d. college.

6. Burt stopped playing football because

   a. he didn't have enough time.
   b. he suffered an injury.
   c. the kids at school were making fun of him.
   d. the other players were making fun of him.

7. While Burt is away, his ranch is taken care of by his

   a. parents.
   b. aunt.
   c. brother.
   d. children.

8. Eventually, Burt would like to try

   a. farming.
   b. writing.
   c. singing.
   d. teaching.

● FIGURING THE FACTS

Decide whether the following statements are true or false. Write **T** on the line if the statement is true. If the statement is false, change the statement to make it true. Cross out the incorrect word or phrase in the sentence. Then, if necessary, write the correct word or phrase on the line.

1. Burt Reynolds isn't the rough guy we see in his movies. _____

2. Instead of his fists, Burt uses his talents to prove himself. _____

3. Burt is an actor and a director. _____

4. In junior high, some kids called Burt "mullet." _____

5. After he won a chess game, Burt's friends stopped calling him names. _____

6. Burt attended Georgia State College. _____

7. Burt is not sorry that he never finished college. _____

8. Burt is now attending college. _____

9. Burt never calls his parents on the telephone. _____

10. At home, Burt's nickname is "Bobby." _____

● WHAT'S YOUR OPINION?

1. Why do you think the kids in Burt's school stopped calling him names after he won the race?

_____
_____
_____
_____
_____

2. Burt always seems to find time to call his parents. Why do you think it is important for people to have a good relationship with their parents?

_____
_____
_____
_____
_____

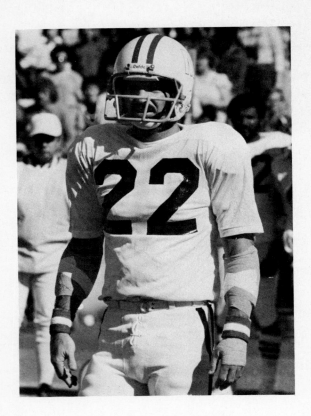

● DEVELOPING SPELLING SKILLS

Study List

activities
apologies
authorities
classified
copied
defying
envying
injuries
magnifying
multiplying
occupied
relying
satisfied
studies
supplied

The following words contain a final *y* that is preceded by a consonant.

       injury   **occupy**   **study**   **rely**

Notice that when we add a suffix to these words, the *y* is changed to *i* except when adding *ing*.

       injuries   **occupied**   **studies**   **relying**

Rule: *When a word ends in* **y** *preceded by a consonant, change the* **y** *to* **i** *before adding any suffix except* **ing.**

As you can see, this rule applies when changing words to the plural as well as when adding other suffixes.

    On your left is a Study List of words. Each has been formed by adding a suffix to a word that ends in *y* preceded by a consonant.

● SKILL DRILL 1

Add the suffix to the word that ends in *y* to form words from the Study List. Remember the *y* to *i* rule. Write your answers on the lines provided.

1. injury + es = _____

2. multiply + ing = _____

3. apology + es = _____

4. satisfy + ed = _____

5. classify + ed = _____

6. supply + ed = _____

7. copy + ed = _____

8. magnify + ing = _____

9. occupy + ed = _____

10. rely + ing = _____

11. authority + es = _____

12. study + es = _____

13. activity + es = _____

14. defy + ing = _____

15. envy + ing = _____

● SKILL DRILL 2

The following are short definitions of words from the Study List. Fill the blanks with words from the Study List that match the definitions. If you need help, check the Mini-Dictionary in the back of this book.

1. Being jealous of another's good fortune _____

2. Officials of the government _____

3. Damages from harms, or hurts _____

4. Depending on or trusting _____

5. Words of pardon for an offense or accident _____

6. Taken up, filled, or lived in _____

7. Increasing in number or amount _____

8. Resisting or challenging authority _____

9. Having made a copy of something _____

10. Making something look bigger than it really is _____

11. Contented or fulfilled _____

12. Vigorous or strenuous actions or movements _____

13. Lessons or school subjects _____

14. Arranged in classes or groups _____

15. Having satisfied a need or provided a quantity of something _____

●**SKILL DRILL 3**

Complete each sentence by adding a suffix to the word in parentheses to form a Study List word.

1. The children left the table completely (satisfy) _____.

2. Tim and Louise expressed their (apology) _____ for the accident.

3. Prisons are full of people who have spent their lives (defy) _____ the law.

4. The books should be (classify) _____ according to title.

5. Please spend at least two hours on your (study) _____ tonight.

6. At the picnic there will be many athletic (activity) _____.

7. There is a small (magnify) _____ glass on the shelf.

8. Agnes (copy) _____ the paragraph word for word.

9. We will be (rely) _____ on the brook for our water supply.

10. Many players suffer (injury) _____ while on the court.

11. Please report any problems to the proper (authority) _____.

12. (Envy) _____ the success of others is a waste of time.

13. Mrs. Anderson (supply) _____ all the students with pencils.

14. The number of weeds in the garden is (multiply) _____ rapidly.

15. The brown house at the end of the street is (occupy) _____.

●**SKILL DRILL 4**

Answer the following questions by using words from the Study List.

Which words end with the suffix *ing*?

1. _____   2. _____

3. _____   4. _____

5. _____

Which words appear in their plural form?

6. _____   7. _____

8. _____   9. _____

10. _____

Which words end with the suffix *ed*?

11. _____   12. _____

13. _____   14. _____

15. _____

● WORD GAME 1

The words from the Study List are hidden in this puzzle. They read from top to bottom, left to right, and diagonally. Circle the words you find, but make sure they are spelled correctly. When you find a word, cross it off the list.

A	M	I	E	R	C	L	A	S	S	I	F	A	R	S	T
S	T	U	D	I	E	S	D	S	U	P	L	P	E	T	A
U	T	B	L	I	M	L	A	G	N	I	F	O	A	U	L
T	D	E	F	T	N	X	Y	I	N	G	B	L	N	D	I
H	A	Y	N	G	I	J	A	I	C	D	E	O	O	Y	S
O	C	I	J	K	L	P	U	H	N	F	G	G	C	I	A
R	T	L	M	N	O	P	L	R	H	G	F	I	C	E	U
I	I	M	A	G	N	I	F	Y	I	N	G	E	U	S	T
T	V	Q	R	S	U	P	P	L	I	E	D	S	P	T	H
I	I	T	U	V	S	D	I	B	E	N	S	C	I	C	O
E	T	W	C	O	P	I	E	D	J	N	G	D	E	I	R
Z	I	C	T	I	Z	K	F	F	U	R	V	E	D	A	I
A	E	M	U	L	T	I	P	I	Y	V	B	I	C	B	T
B	S	S	A	T	I	S	F	Y	E	I	I	T	E	I	I
C	D	S	A	T	I	S	F	I	E	D	N	E	S	S	E
F	E	G	H	I	J	E	N	V	Y	I	N	G	K	L	S

Study List

activities
apologies
authorities
classified
copied
defying
envying
injuries
magnifying
multiplying
occupied
relying
satisfied
studies
supplied

● HOW WELL CAN YOU SPELL?

Try to take this practice test without looking back at Lesson 1. After you have finished, check your work against the Study List. Correct any mistakes you have made.

A. One word in each of the following pairs of words is spelled incorrectly. Circle that word and spell it correctly on the line provided.

1. satisfyed, studies   _____

2. activities, enving   _____

3. magnifing, copied   _____

4. classified, defing   _____

5. occupied, apologyies   _____

6. supplyed, relying   _____

7. multiplying, authoritys   _____

8. injuryes, activity   _____

B. In each of the following sentences, one word is spelled incorrectly. Find that word. Then spell it correctly on the line provided.

9. The fire victims are reling on the government for support. _____

10. Club members are classifyed according to their age.   _____

11. There will be several activitys scheduled for the party.   _____

12. George will return to his studyes next week.   _____

13. That picture was copied from a magazine cover.   _____

14. Tennis occupyied much of their vacation time.   _____

15. The problem can be solved by multipling the last two numbers.   _____

2 Up in Smoke

The sight of typewritten words probably doesn't stop you in your tracks. But the sight of a typewritten message across the sky very well might. That's why Greg Stinis and his skytypers have gone to the air. They want their words to be hard to miss.

Skytyping is not as common as skywriting but it's being used more and more. Skywriters make written words. Skytypers make printed words to display their messages. The art of skytyping was invented in 1949. The skytypers use World War II planes because they have large engines that make great amounts of heat. The heat is needed to melt a substance called paraffin. This process results in a white smoke that is used to write messages.

The skytypers employ a series of dashes to form letters. They fly five planes in close formation. A computer-controlled device automatically lets out puffs of smoke from each of the planes at the same time. These puffs form letters. Each letter is as large as the Empire State Building—1,200 feet (365 meters) tall. These heavenly billboards often stretch over five miles (eight km.) of sky! Skytyped words can relay a message to those miles away. On a clear day millions of people can see one skytyped message.

Greg and the other four skytypers often write ads for suntan lotion, cars, cameras, films, and records. And for those who easily tire of greeting cards, the skytypers have written countless "Happy Birthdays," "I Love You's," and "Congratulations." Once, they even played a flying tic-tac-toe game! Skytyping will probably be around for a long time. The message is hard to miss!

● REVIEWING YOUR READING

Circle the letter beside the word or phrase that best completes the sentence.

1. Skytyping was invented in

    a. 1449.
    b. 1494.
    c. 1949.
    d. 1994.

2. The skytypers use World War II planes because they

    a. fly at a faster speed than other planes.
    b. fly at a higher altitude than other planes.
    c. make great amounts of electricity.
    d. make great amounts of heat.

3. The skytypers fly

    a. five planes in close formation.
    b. ten planes in close formation.
    c. fifteen planes in close formation.
    d. twenty planes in close formation.

4. The puffs of smoke are released by

    a. a person in the rear of the plane.
    b. a computer-controlled instrument.
    c. the wings.
    d. the wheels.

5. Skytyped letters are as large as

    a. the Statue of Liberty.
    b. the Empire State Building.
    c. an airplane.
    d. a billboard.

6. To form letters, skytypers employ a series of

    a. curved lines.
    b. loops and swirls.
    c. dashes.
    d. dots and curves.

7. According to the story, you can conclude that

    a. skytyping is different from skywriting.
    b. skytyping is out of style.
    c. skywriting is the newest type of advertisement.
    d. skywriting is done from the ground.

8. Another title for this story could be

    a. Greg Stinis—Skytyper.
    b. Skytyping.
    c. Skywriting.
    d. The Flying Tic-tac-toe Game.

● FIGURING THE FACTS

Decide whether the following statements are true or false. Write **T** on the line if the statement is true. If the statement is false, change the statement to make it true. Cross out the incorrect word or phrase in the sentence. Then, if necessary, write the correct word or phrase on the line.

1. Skytyping is being used less and less these days.   _____

2. The skytyping planes release black smoke.   _____

3. The smoke is produced from paraffin.   _____

4. Skytyping is more common than skywriting.   _____

5. The puffs of smoke form letters.   _____

6. A skytyped message is printed close to the ground.   _____

7. The skytypers fly seven planes in formation.   _____

8. On a clear day millions of people can see one skytyped message.   _____

9. Skytypers never print ads.   _____

10. The story tells us that there was once a flying chess game.   _____

● WHAT'S YOUR OPINION?

1. Why do you think skytyping is becoming so popular?

_____

_____

_____

2. Do you think reading a skytyped message is more exciting than reading a message written on paper? Why or why not?

_____

_____

_____

_____

● **DEVELOPING SPELLING SKILLS**

Study List

The following words appear in the reading selection.

display   employ   relay

All of these words contain a final *y* that is preceded by a vowel. Notice in the Study List words that when we add a suffix, the *y* remains the same.

Rule: *When a word ends in a final* **y** *that is preceded by a vowel, the word is not changed when adding a suffix. (This rule also applies when forming the plural of the word.)*

Examples: displaying   employers   relayed

On your left is a Study List of words. Each has been formed by adding a suffix to a word that ends in a final *y* preceded by a vowel.

alloys
annoyance
betrayed
conveying
decayed
decoys
destroyed
disobeyed
displaying
employer
journeys
relaying
strayed
surveying
swaying

● SKILL DRILL 1

Add the suffix to the word ending in *y* to form words from the Study List. Write your answers on the lines provided.

1. display + ing = _____

2. journey + s = _____

3. survey + ing = _____

4. sway + ing = _____

5. annoy + ance = _____

6. convey + ing = _____

7. decoy + s = _____

8. employ + er = _____

9. relay + ing = _____

10. stray + ed = _____

11. alloy + s = _____

12. betray + ed = _____

13. decay + ed = _____

14. destroy + ed = _____

15. disobey + ed = _____

● SKILL DRILL 2

The following are short definitions of words from the Study List. Fill the blanks with words from the Study List that match the definitions. If you need help, check the Mini-Dictionary in the back of this book.

1. Metals made by mixing two or more metals _____

2. Transporting or carrying something—a word that means the same as relaying _____

3. Was unfaithful to something or gave away a secret _____

4. Swinging back and forth _____

5. Wandered or roamed away _____

6. Refused or failed to obey _____

7. Taking something and carrying it farther—a word that means the same as conveying _____

8. Long trips or travels _____

9. A person or firm that hires someone to work _____

10. Rotted, losing strength or beauty _____

11. Things used to lure or tempt someone into danger _____

12. Something that bothers or disturbs you _____

13. Showing or exposing to view _____

14. Broken into pieces; ended _____

15. Looking over or viewing something; skimming _____

● SKILL DRILL 3

Complete each sentence by adding a suffix to the word in parentheses to form a Study List word.

1. The workers will be (survey) _____ the land tomorrow.

2. Tom (disobey) _____ the traffic rule by jay walking.

3. The puppies (stray) _____ onto the beach.

4. The cypress trees are (sway) _____ in the breeze.

5. The trucks will be (convey) _____ these supplies.

6. Elaine (betray) _____ the trust of her friends.

7. These metals are (alloy) _____ .

8. Mrs. Smith (destroy) _____ the copy of the letter.

9. The department store will be (display) _____ the product tomorrow.

10. Those airplanes are an (annoy) _____ to the students.

11. The hunters hid their (decoy) _____ under the bushes.

12. Ralph's back teeth have become (decay) _____ from not brushing.

13. This company is an equal opportunity (employ) _____ .

14. The club has taken many (journey) _____ to the seaside.

15. These wires are always (relay) _____ messages across the country.

● SKILL DRILL 4

Answer the following questions by using words from the Study List.

Which words end with the suffix *ing*?

1. _____   2. _____

3. _____   4. _____

5. _____

Which word ends with the suffix *er*?

6. _____

Which words appear in their plural form?

7. _____   8. _____

9. _____

Which words end with the suffix *ed*?

10. _____   11. _____

12. _____   13. _____

14. _____

Which word ends with the suffix *ance*?

15. _____

● WORD GAME 2

All of the letters from the words in the Study List appear in this puzzle. Cross out the letters of the puzzle as you use them to spell the Study List words. There will be enough letters left over to answer the question below.

Study List

			A	A	A					
		A	A	A	A	A				
	A	B	B	C	C	C				
D	D	D	D	D	D	D	D			
D	E	E	E	E	E	E	E	E	E	
E	E	E	E	E	E	G	G	G	G	I
I	I	I	I	I	I	J	L	L	L	L	M
N	N	N	N	N	N	N	N	O	O	O
O	O	O	O	P	P	P	R	R	R	R
R	R	S	S	S	S	S	S	S	S
T	T	T	U	U	U	V	W
Y	Y	Y	Y	Y	Y	Y
Y	Y	Y	Y	Y
Y	Y	Y

alloys
annoyance
betrayed
conveying
decayed
decoys
destroyed
disobeyed
displaying
employer
journeys
relaying
strayed
surveying
swaying

Where would you begin to look to find the skytypers? _____

● **HOW WELL CAN YOU SPELL?**

Try to take this practice test without looking back at Lesson 2. After you have finished, check your work against the Study List. Correct any mistakes you have made.

A. One word in each of the following pairs of words is spelled incorrectly. Circle that word and spell it correctly on the line provided.

1. conveing, swaying   _____

2. displaying, disobeyied   _____

3. decaied, relayed   _____

4. destroyed, annoiance   _____

5. betrayed, journies   _____

6. decoyies, strayed   _____

7. alloyies, employer   _____

8. surveing, relaying   _____

B. In each of the following sentences, one word is spelled incorrectly. Find the word. Then spell it correctly on the line provided.

9. The storm destroyied all of the homes on the coast.   _____

10. The students are proudly displaing their school colors. _____

11. The wind was so strong, even the telephone poles
     were swaing.   _____

12. The robber's innocence was betrayied by the mud on
     his shoes.   _____

13. Three young scouts strayied away from camp today.   _____

14. This employier is very generous to the workers.   _____

15. The girls will be relaing the message at the meeting.   _____

3 Cliff Hanger

"The way to eat an elephant is one bite at a time." Those were the words Beverly Johnson repeated to herself. Inch by inch she made her way up the steep mountain wall in California's Yosemite National Park. Beverly Johnson was climbing a cliff called El Capitan. It is one of the most overpowering walls in the world. From bottom to top the distance is 3,604 feet (1,098 meters). That's as long as ten football fields—straight up! Beverly Johnson climbed the mighty cliff alone! She is the first woman ever to do so.

The climb usually requires a team of two or three people. And it takes about a week to reach the top. Six months before Beverly's adventure, three climbers tried to conquer El Capitan. They fell to their deaths.

The "solo" trip for Beverly was doubly difficult. She first had to climb about 100 feet (30 meters). That was her first "pitch." Climbers measure how far they are climbing by what they call "pitches." A "pitch" is usually the length of their safety ropes. Beverly then drove a metal stake called a piton into the rock. After attaching her ropes to the piton, she lowered herself back down to get her gear. She then went back up, fastened her gear, and started to work on her next "pitch." She had to go up and down each pitch twice, pulling out the metal stakes as she went. Beverly made 27 pitches in all.

Her pouch of supplies included cheeses, fruits, water, and a "bat tent." That's a type of hammock that is anchored to the wall. Beverly made no comment about how well she slept hanging off the cliff. But during her climb, a small earthquake took place. When asked if she felt the quake, Beverly replied, "No, I thought it might have been my knees shaking."

● REVIEWING YOUR READING

Circle the letter beside the word or phrase that best completes the sentence.

1. Beverly Johnson climbed a

   a. tall building.
   b. mountain wall.
   c. football stadium.
   d. large tree.

2. Beverly made her climb

   a. alone.
   b. with one other person.
   c. with two other people.
   d. with three other people.

3. Three climbers fell off the cliff

   a. six years before Beverly's climb.
   b. six months before Beverly's climb.
   c. after Beverly's climb.
   d. during Beverly's climb.

4. Climbers measure how far they are climbing by what they call

   a. pitons.
   b. gear.
   c. lengths.
   d. pitches.

5. Beverly's climb was doubly difficult because she had to

   a. take twice the gear.
   b. go up and down each "pitch" twice.
   c. bring twice as much food with her.
   d. drive in twice as many pitons.

6. A piton is a

   a. rope.
   b. pitch.
   c. metal stake.
   d. hammer.

7. During Beverly's climb there was

   a. an earthquake.
   b. a tornado.
   c. a thunderstorm.
   d. a snowstorm.

8. According to the story, you can conclude that Beverly

   a. enjoys risk and adventure.
   b. is afraid of heights.
   c. is not athletic.
   d. prefers to climb with a large group of people.

● FIGURING THE FACTS

Decide whether the following statements are true or false. Write **T** on the line if the statement is true. If the statement is false, change the statement to make it true. Cross out the incorrect word or phrase in the sentence. Then, if necessary, write the correct word or phrase on the line.

1. The cliff Beverly climbed was called "Elephant."   _____

2. The cliff is as long as ten football fields.   _____

3. Beverly made her climb in Yosemite National Park.   _____

4. It usually takes about three weeks to reach the top.   _____

5. A pitch is usually the length of a climber's tent.   _____

6. Beverly made her climb in one pitch.   _____

7. Beverly's supplies included cheeses, fruits, and water.   _____

8. At night, Beverly slept in a cat tent.   _____

9. Beverly said she slept while hanging off the cliff.   _____

10. During her climb, Beverly felt an earthquake.   _____

● WHAT'S YOUR OPINION?

1. What do you think Beverly meant when she said, "The way to eat an elephant is one bite at a time"?

_____

_____

_____

_____

_____

2. If you could be the first person to climb a mountain alone, would you do it? Why or why not?

_____

_____

_____

_____

● DEVELOPING SPELLING SKILLS

In this lesson we will look at how to change some words to the plural form. For example, we know that to change a word that ends in *y* like *apology* to the plural, we change the final *y* to *i* and add *es*. The plural of *apology* is *apologies*. In the next few chapters we will be learning the different ways that words become plural.

Study List

Singular	Plural
adventure	adventures
ambulance	ambulances
budget	budgets
characteristic	characteristics
cheese	cheeses
crutch	crutches
hatchet	hatchets
inch	inches
opinion	opinions
pouch	pouches
radish	radishes
sandwich	sandwiches
sheriff	sheriffs
sketch	sketches
stitch	stitches

Most words form their plural by adding *s* to the singular form.

Examples:

Singular	Plural
adventure	adventures
budget	budgets
cheese	cheeses

But words that end in *ch* or *sh* form their plurals by adding *es*.

Examples:

Singular	Plural
inch	inches
pouch	pouches
radish	radishes

Rule: *If a word ends in* **ch** *or* **sh**, *the plural is formed by adding* **es**.

On your left is a Study List of words. Both the singular and plural forms are listed. It is important to know both.

● SKILL DRILL 1

Change each of the following singular nouns to the plural. Write your answers on the lines provided.

1. hatchet _____
2. sandwich _____
3. sketch _____
4. inch _____
5. pouch _____
6. ambulance _____
7. characteristic _____

8. radish _____
9. sheriff _____
10. stitch _____
11. opinion _____
12. adventure _____
13. budget _____
14. cheese _____

15. crutch _____

● SKILL DRILL 2

The following are short definitions of words from the Study List. The definitions are of the words in their singular form. Write the *singular form* of the Study List word that matches the definition. If you need help, check the Mini-Dictionary in the back of this book.

1. A solid food made from milk _____
2. A plan for spending time or money _____
3. A vehicle used to carry sick people _____
4. An unusual or exciting experience _____
5. A law enforcement officer _____
6. A support to help a lame person walk _____
7. A rough or quickly done drawing _____
8. A loop of thread made while sewing _____
9. Two slices of bread with filling between such as meat or cheese _____
10. A small, crisp, red vegetable _____
11. A bag or sack _____
12. What a person thinks _____
13. A measure of length _____
14. A quality that shows how a person or thing is different from others _____
15. A small axe that is used with one hand _____

● SKILL DRILL 3

Fill in each blank with the plural of the noun in parentheses to form a Study List word.

1. Help yourself to the (cheese) _____.

2. The (stitch) _____ in my jacket are coming apart.

3. Please get Janice her (crutch) _____.

4. Milk and some (sandwich) _____ are in the refrigerator.

5. Dad pulled the two (hatchet) _____ out of the tree.

6. What this salad needs is some (radish) _____.

7. Kangaroos are one of the few animals with (pouch) _____.

8. The students gave their (opinion) _____ at the meeting.

9. Next year the clerks will have to balance their (budget) _____.

10. There was a line of (ambulance) _____ outside the hospital.

11. Each day is full of (adventure) _____, if you look for them.

12. Seven (sheriff) _____ will be at the meeting.

13. The artist showed us several (sketch) _____.

14. She is three (inch) _____ taller than I.

15. Courtesy and friendliness are the (characteristic) _____ of a good salesperson.

● SKILL DRILL 4

Answer the following questions by using the plural form of words from the Study List.

Which words end with the letters *ts*?

1. _____   2. _____

Which word ends with the letters *shes*?

3. _____

Which words end with the letters *ches*?

4. _____   5. _____

6. _____   7. _____

8. _____   9. _____

Which word ends with the letters *ses*?

10. _____

Which word ends with the letters *ces*?

11. _____

Which word ends with the letters *ns*?

12. _____

Which word ends with the letters *res*?

13. _____

Which word ends with the letters *fs*?

14. _____

Which word ends with the letters *cs*?

15. _____

Study List

adventures
ambulances
budgets
characteristics
cheeses
crutches
hatchets
inches
opinions
pouches
radishes
sandwiches
sheriffs
sketches
stitches

● **WORD GAME 3**

The plural form of the words from the Study List are scrambled on the left. Unscramble each word and write it correctly in the spaces on the right. If you unscramble the words correctly, you will find the answer to the puzzle question by reading the shaded column downward. Write your answer on the line below.

S N O P O N I I

S D T V A E N U E R

S E C S E H E

S O H C E P U

S T I H C S E T

S E H C T E K S

S I N E H C

S C A R A H C C I T R E T I S

S R D A I S H E

S T A H C H E T

S C H I D A N W S E

S T H C U R C E

S F I R H E F S

S N A L U B M A E C

S U B G D T E

How did Beverly Johnson make it up El Capitan? _____

● HOW WELL CAN YOU SPELL?

Try to take this practice test without looking back at Lesson 3. After you have finished, check your work against the Study List. Correct any mistakes you have made.

A. One word in each of the following pairs of words is spelled incorrectly. Circle that word and spell it correctly on the line provided.

1. ambulanses, sandwiches   _____

2. inches, sheriffes   _____

3. characteristices, radishes   _____

4. pouchs, hatchets   _____

5. opinions, crutchs   _____

6. stitchs, cheeses   _____

7. adventurs, ambulances   _____

8. budgetes, sketches   _____

B. In each of the following sentences, one word is spelled incorrectly. Find that word. Then spell it correctly on the line provided.

9. Thelma has several opiniones on that subject.   _____

10. We will be having peanut butter sandwichs for lunch. _____

11. Shirley needs a few more inchs of ribbon for the package. _____

12. Be sure to buy some radishs at the market.   _____

13. Ken will be serving fruits and cheesees tonight.   _____

14. The art class will be doing sketchs this week.   _____

15. The workers found several old hatchetes in the basement. _____

4 The Moose Is Loose!

You'll find them roaming hills and valleys from Alaska and British Columbia, to Nova Scotia and Maine. Their deep bellow can be heard for miles around. Some people describe the noise as a deep a-e-i-o-u. It may sound terrible to you and me, but to another moose it means "hello"!

The moose is the largest member of the deer family. Moose can weigh up to a ton. With all that weight, you'd think they would have difficulty moving at all. But they can run at speeds of 35 miles (56 kilometers) per hour! During the warm weather months, moose like to be near water. They are excellent swimmers, able to travel for a dozen miles (nineteen kilometers) without stopping. They are even good at high diving. Some moose can dive from heights of 20 feet (6 meters)!

Each spring, the male, or bull moose, grows a crown of majestic antlers. Unlike the horns of other animals, which are hardened skin, moose antlers are made entirely of bone. Aside from their beauty, they also serve a purpose. Antlers attract females. In addition, they are used as weapons. If one bull tries to steal another bull's mate, trouble begins. Sometimes moose lock horns in battle. But more often than not, they shake the bushes with their antlers and make a lot of noise! This is supposed to frighten the intruder. It seems that even the moose like to avoid fighting! When first grown, moose antlers are covered with a velvet-like skin. Eventually, the moose will rub them against trees to remove the "velvet." Then the white bone will become stained brown. When winter comes and the antlers are no longer needed, the moose sheds them. As spring approaches, the cycle starts anew.

Although moose are now plentiful, they were once in danger of extinction. Thanks to conservation, these grand creatures still roam North America.

● REVIEWING YOUR READING

Circle the letter beside the word or phrase that best completes the sentence.

1. Moose can be found living in

   a. South America.
   b. North America.
   c. Mexico.
   d. the southern United States.

2. The noise a moose makes can be described as

   a. a high sharp sound.
   b. a loud coughing noise.
   c. a hooting sound.
   d. a deep bellow.

3. During the summer, moose like to be near

   a. mountains.
   b. valleys.
   c. water.
   d. caves.

4. Some moose can

   a. swim for 50 miles (80.4 kilometers).
   b. dive 20 feet (6 meters).
   c. swim 100 miles (160.9 kilometers).
   d. dive 135 feet (41.1 meters).

5. Moose antlers are made entirely of

   a. bone.
   b. skin.
   c. wood.
   d. velvet.

6. Each year the moose

   a. grows a new set of antlers.
   b. sheds his fur.
   c. sheds his skin.
   d. grows longer antlers.

7. You can come to the conclusion that male moose

   a. enjoy fighting.
   b. probably don't like to fight.
   c. are afraid of water.
   d. are afraid of noise.

8. You can come to the conclusion that

   a. there are only a few moose still living.
   b. there are many moose in the wild.
   c. moose are now extinct.
   d. moose were once extinct.

● FIGURING THE FACTS

Decide whether the following statements are true or false. Write **T** on the line if the statement is true. If the statement is false, change the statement to make it true. Cross out the incorrect word or phrase in the sentence. Then, if necessary, write the correct word or phrase on the line.

1. The male moose is called a bull. _____

2. The moose often makes a sound like an owl. _____

3. A moose can swim for many miles. _____

4. The moose may be found in Nova Scotia. _____

5. The moose's antlers are used to pick food. _____

6. Sometimes the antlers are used as weapons. _____

7. Moose antlers are exactly like other animals' horns. _____

8. Antlers are sometimes covered with velvet-like skin. _____

9. Female moose sometimes lock horns in battle. _____

10. A moose can run 35 miles (56 kilometers) per hour. _____

● WHAT'S YOUR OPINION?

1. At one time the moose was almost extinct. Why is it important to help and protect animals?

_____

_____

_____

_____

2. The moose only fights when he has to. Do you think this is a good way to be? Why?

_____

_____

_____

_____

_____

● DEVELOPING SPELLING SKILLS

In this lesson we will review the rules we've learned about plural forms. We will also learn a new rule that explains how words ending in *x* form the plural.

Rule: *Words that end in* **x** *form their plural by adding* **es.**

Study List

Singular	Plural
activity	activities
ambulance	ambulances
bush	bushes
class	classes
fox	foxes
hatchet	hatchets
magazine	magazines
match	matches
parade	parades
reflex	reflexes
schedule	schedules
speech	speeches
trophy	trophies
valley	valleys
wish	wishes

Example:

Singular	Plural
reflex	reflexes

Here is a review of the other rules we've learned.

Rule: *Most words form their plural by adding* **s** *to the singular form.*

Example:

Singular	Plural
parade	parades

Rule: *Words that end in* **ch** *or* **sh** *form their plural by adding* **es.**

Example:

Singular	Plural
match	matches

Rule: *Words that end in* **y** *preceded by a consonant change the* **y** *to* **i** *and add* **es.**

Example:

Singular	Plural
activity	activities

Above is a Study List of words. Both singular and plural forms are listed. As you look at each word in the Study List, try to remember which of the rules mentioned above applies to the plural form.

● SKILL DRILL 1

Change each of the following singular nouns to the plural. Write your answers on the lines provided.

1. parade _____   8. reflex _____
2. schedule _____   9. speech _____
3. trophy _____   10. valley _____
4. activity _____   11. ambulance _____
5. bush _____   12. class _____
6. fox _____   13. hatchet _____
7. magazine _____   14. match _____

15. wish _____

● SKILL DRILL 2

The following are short definitions of words from the Study List. The definitions are of the words in their singular form. Write the *singular form* of the Study List word that matches the definition. If you need help, check the Mini-Dictionary in the back of this book.

1. A public talk _____

2. A written or printed statement of details _____

3. An automatic response _____

4. A march or display _____

5. A wild animal that is sly and crafty _____

6. A meeting of a group of students and a teacher _____

7. A woody plant that is smaller than a tree _____

8. Vehicle used to carry sick people _____

9. Vigorous or strenuous action or movement _____

10. A person or thing that goes well with another person or thing _____

11. A regular publication containing stories and articles _____

12. A small axe that is used with one hand _____

13. An expression of a desire or want _____

14. Low land between hills or mountains _____

15. A prize for the winner of a contest _____

● SKILL DRILL 3

Fill in each blank with the plural of the noun in parentheses to form a Study List word.

1. There will be two (trophy) _____ for each winner.

2. Debbie would like to stay and listen to the (speech) _____ .

3. When you're at the train station, please pick up some (schedule) _____ .

4. Would you like some (magazine) _____ to read on the plane?

5. We will need a few (hatchet) _____ for cutting these trees.

6. Twirlers must have good (reflex) _____ .

7. There will be three (parade) _____ on Tuesday.

8. We have a family of (fox) _____ living behind the house.

9. The camp has many (activity) _____ for the students.

10. In the play, the colors of the girls' dresses were good (match) _____.

11. The art (class) _____ will be meeting next week.

12. Ed got a job trimming the (bush) _____ in the park.

13. Our hospital has several (ambulance) _____ ready for emergencies.

14. I hope that all of Joan's (wish) _____ come true.

15. On the other side of those hills, there are several large (valley) _____ .

●SKILL DRILL 4

Answer the following questions by using words from the Study List.

Which words end in *xes*?

1. _____   2. _____

Which words end in *ches*?

3. _____   4. _____

Which words end in *shes*?

5. _____   6. _____

Which word ends in *ses*?   Which word ends in *ces*?

7. _____   8. _____

Which word ends in *eys*?   Which word ends in *les*?

9. _____   10. _____

Which word ends in *nes*?   Which word ends in *des*?

11. _____   12. _____

Which words end in *ies*?

13. _____   14. _____

Which word ends in *ets*?

15. _____

● WORD GAME 4

The plural words from the Study List are hidden in this puzzle. They read from top to bottom, left to right, and diagonally. Circle the words you find. Make sure they are spelled correctly. When you find a word, cross it off the list.

Study List

Singular	Plural
activity	activities
ambulance	ambulances
bush	bushes
class	classes
fox	foxes
hatchet	hatchets
magazine	magazines
match	matches
parade	parades
reflex	reflexes
schedule	schedules
speech	speeches
trophy	trophies
valley	valleys
wish	wishes

A	M	A	T	C	H	E	S	A	D	V	E	T	S
M	H	T	F	S	L	T	M	A	T	C	S	E	T
B	T	P	L	O	E	A	R	C	O	U	H	S	H
U	R	L	M	I	X	N	S	O	P	S	H	P	A
L	O	V	A	L	L	E	Y	S	U	I	E	E	C
A	P	H	G	L	O	R	S	B	E	S	R	E	T
P	H	P	A	R	A	D	E	S	T	S	L	C	I
H	I	V	Z	T	N	W	X	F	S	L	O	H	V
I	E	M	I	E	C	A	I	Y	L	W	O	E	I
E	S	G	N	R	K	H	A	S	R	E	D	S	T
S	C	H	E	D	U	L	E	S	H	S	X	O	I
R	E	F	S	E	R	P	I	T	N	E	S	E	E
A	M	B	U	L	A	N	C	E	S	H	S	M	S

● HOW WELL CAN YOU SPELL?

Try to take this practice test without looking back at Lesson 4. After you have finished, check your work against the Study List. Correct any mistakes you have made.

A. One word in each of the following pairs of words is spelled incorrectly. Circle that word and spell it correctly on the line provided.

1. wishs, magazines   _____

2. hatchetes, parades   _____

3. activity, foxs   _____

4. reflexs, trophies   _____

5. matches, ambulancies   _____

6. vallies, bushes   _____

7. classes, scheduls   _____

8. speechs, parade   _____

B. In each of the following sentences, one word is spelled incorrectly. Find that word. Then spell it correctly on the line provided.

9. There will be several activitys scheduled for today.   _____

10. Elaine has twelve trophys in her collection.   _____

11. Baton twirlers are often seen performing in parads.   _____

12. Jack left the magazins on the shelf in the library.   _____

13. The frightened animal was hiding in the bushs.   _____

14. Don't forget to write the speaches!   _____

15. My cooking classis will begin early next week.   _____

5 Cowkids

A proud horse prances into the arena. Its rider struggles to hold a huge American flag that snaps in the breeze. Echoes of "Yahoo" and "Yippee" explode from the crowd. Parading close behind is a seemingly endless line of riders on horseback. Friendly young faces shine from beneath ten-gallon hats. As at any other rodeo, there are pens of horses and buffaloes, and cowpokes sitting on wood fences. But this event is something very special. It is the National High School Rodeo.

Each year since 1949, teenagers from all over the United States and Canada have come together for the world's largest rodeo. They meet to pick the best all-round cowkids, and to have an all-round good time.

Some of the events include calf roping and steer wrestling. One of the wildest competitions is reserved for cowgirls only. It's called goat tying. To begin, a goat is placed in the middle of the arena. The contestant races to the goat on horseback. She must jump off the horse, catch the goat, and throw it down. Then she must tie three of the goat's legs together. Of course, the goat is not very happy about being tied up. The result is usually a tornado of dust and flying hooves.

A time of ten seconds in the goat tying event is considered to be very quick. But a teenager named Barrie Beach has done it in eight seconds! For three years in a row, she has won the goat tying competition. Barrie gets plenty of practice. She ties goats for four hours every day—before breakfast!

Why does she do it? "I'm a competitor," Barrie says. And that's what the National High School Rodeo is all about—competition. There are over a thousand competitors in all, and the number is growing every year. Ride 'em, cowkids!

● **REVIEWING YOUR READING**

Circle the letter beside the word or phrase that best completes the sentence.

1. The National High School Rodeo begins with a

    a. movie.
    b. parade.
    c. fireworks display.
    d. race.

2. The teenagers who take part in the rodeo are all from

    a. Canada.
    b. Kansas.
    c. the United States.
    d. the United States and Canada.

3. The goat tying competition is reserved for

    a. cowgirls only.
    b. cowboys only.
    c. goats only.
    d. adults only.

4. In the goat tying competition, contestants race to the goat on

    a. goats.
    b. mules.
    c. donkeys.
    d. horses.

5. Barrie Beach won the goat tying competition for

    a. three years in a row.
    b. five years in a row.
    c. eight years in a row.
    d. ten years in a row.

6. Barrie usually gets her practice

    a. in the early evening.
    b. in the afternoon.
    c. in the morning.
    d. at night.

7. According to the story, you can conclude that Barrie

    a. sleeps late.
    b. gets up early.
    c. stays up late.
    d. sleeps until noon.

8. According to the story, you can conclude that teenagers take part in the rodeo because they like to

    a. feed the animals.
    b. march in parades.
    c. compete.
    d. tie up the animals.

● FIGURING THE FACTS

Decide whether the following statements are true or false. Write **T** on the line if the statement is true. If the statement is false, change the statement to make it true. Cross out the incorrect word or phrase in the sentence. Then, if necessary, write the correct word or phrase on the line.

1. At a rodeo, you might see cowpokes sitting on wood fences. _____

2. The National High School Rodeo is the world's smallest rodeo. _____

3. The National High School Rodeo has been happening since 1949. _____

4. One of the fastest events is the calf relay race. _____

5. There are over three million competitors at the rodeo. _____

6. In goat tying, all four of the goat's legs must be tied. _____

7. Barrie Beach practices tying for four hours a day. _____

8. The goats do not like to be tied up. _____

9. The number of contestants in the rodeo is growing every year. _____

10. Barrie Beach has tied up a goat in two seconds. _____

● WHAT'S YOUR OPINION?

1. Why do you think more and more teenagers are getting involved in the rodeo?

_____

_____

_____

_____

2. During the rodeo, the animals are not hurt. Do you think it is all right to tie up the animals? Why or why not?

_____

_____

_____

_____

● DEVELOPING SPELLING SKILLS

When changing words to the plural, we must be especially careful of words that end with the letter *o*. Here are some words taken from the reading selection. Some form plurals differently from others.

Study List

Singular	Plural
banjo	banjos
buffalo	buffaloes
hero	heroes
piano	pianos
portfolio	portfolios
potato	potatoes
radio	radios
rodeo	rodeos
shampoo	shampoos
soprano	sopranos
stereo	stereos
studio	studios
tomato	tomatoes
tornado	tornadoes
volcano	volcanoes

Examples:

Singular	Plural
rodeo	rodeos
buffalo	buffaloes
tornado	tornadoes

Notice that the word *rodeo* forms its plural by simply adding *s*. The words *tornado* and *buffalo* form their plurals by adding *es*. This is because *tornado* and *buffalo* end in *o* preceded by a consonant. Remember: *a, e, i, o, u,* and sometimes *y* are vowels. All the other letters of the alphabet are consonants.

Rule: *If a noun ends in* **o** *preceded by a vowel, add* **s** *to form the plural. If a noun ends in* **o** *preceded by a consonant, add* **es** *to form the plural.*

Exception: *Musical terms and instruments that end in* **o** *form their plurals by adding* **s**. *For example: banjos, pianos, or sopranos.*

Above is a Study List of words. Both the singular and plural forms are listed. It is most important to know both.

● SKILL DRILL 1

Circle the last two letters in each of the following words. Then write the plural form of each word on the line provided.

1. rodeo   _____
2. potato   _____
3. piano   _____
4. stereo   _____
5. buffalo   _____
6. volcano   _____
7. tomato   _____

8. radio   _____
9. portfolio   _____
10. studio   _____
11. hero   _____
12. banjo   _____
13. tornado   _____
14. soprano   _____

15. shampoo   _____

● SKILL DRILL 2

The following are short definitions of words from the Study List. The definitions are for the words in their singular form. Write the *singular form* of the Study List word that matches the definition. If you need help, check the Mini-Dictionary in the back of this book.

1. A soap used to wash hair   _____
2. A contest in riding horses or roping cattle   _____
3. A large, shaggy animal with strong legs; a bison   _____
4. A way of sending or receiving sounds by electric waves   _____
5. A white vegetable   _____
6. A portable case for papers, or a brief case   _____
7. A juicy, red vegetable   _____
8. A violent and destructive storm; a whirlwind   _____
9. A large musical instrument played by striking the keys on its keyboard   _____
10. A workroom for a painter or other artist   _____
11. A person admired for bravery or great deeds   _____
12. A record player or radio that brings sound from two directions   _____
13. A singer with the highest singing voice there is   _____
14. A hand-held, stringed musical instrument   _____
15. A mountain that expels steam and lava   _____

● **SKILL DRILL 3**

Fill in each blank with the plural of the noun in parentheses to form a Study List word.

1. This afternoon we will go shopping for (radio) _____ .

2. Many (tornado) _____ have been spotted in the Kansas area.

3. This year's crop of (tomato) _____ will be excellent.

4. Art students may leave their (portfolio) _____ in the hall.

5. The dinner will include fish and (potato) _____ .

6. There are still many (buffalo) _____ roaming the West.

7. Ginny has been attending (rodeo) _____ since she was three.

8. There are several (stereo) _____ to choose from.

9. All of the astronauts are (hero) _____ .

10. There are several (volcano) _____ on the island.

11. Auditions for (soprano) _____ will be held today.

12. We have two (studio) _____ available in this building.

13. The orchestra will be using two (piano) _____ .

14. You will find several (shampoo) _____ on the shelf.

15. For the duet, we will need two (banjo) _____ .

● **SKILL DRILL 4**

Answer the following questions by using words from the Study List. You must write both the singular and plural forms.

Singular	**Plural**

Which three words are either musical instruments or musical terms?

1. _____ _____

2. _____ _____

3. _____ _____

Which words are not musical terms but end in an *o* preceded by a consonant?

4. _____ _____

5. _____ _____

	Singular		Plural

6. _____   _____

7. _____   _____

8. _____   _____

9. _____   _____

Which words end in *o* preceded by a vowel?

10. _____   _____

11. _____   _____

12. _____   _____

13. _____   _____

14. _____   _____

15. _____   _____

● **WORD GAME 5**

The plurals of words from the Study List are hidden in this puzzle. They read from top to bottom, left to right, and diagonally. Circle the words you find. Make sure they are spelled correctly. When you find a word, cross it off the list.

Study List

banjos
buffaloes
heroes
pianos
portfolios
potatoes
radios
rodeos
shampoos
sopranos
stereos
studios
tomatoes
tornadoes
volcanoes

V	O	L	C	A	B	U	F	F	A	L	G	Y	S	O
B	S	S	L	T	P	O	R	T	F	O	L	I	O	S
U	A	V	O	V	O	L	C	A	N	O	E	S	P	P
F	K	N	P	T	L	M	S	S	D	I	O	L	R	E
F	J	S	J	O	F	I	A	S	A	I	P	S	A	P
A	O	H	N	O	R	O	E	T	D	T	O	D	N	I
L	S	A	B	A	S	O	H	U	O	P	E	S	O	A
O	P	M	N	J	T	S	T	E	R	E	O	S	S	N
E	I	P	O	A	V	S	T	O	R	N	S	A	D	O
S	M	O	T	O	P	R	A	N	R	O	D	E	O	S
A	T	O	S	T	O	R	N	A	D	O	E	S	O	R
X	P	S	B	L	U	F	F	A	L	O	S	S	T	A

● HOW WELL CAN YOU SPELL?

Try to take this practice test without looking back at Lesson 5. After you have finished, check your work against the Study List. Correct any mistakes you have made.

A. One word in each of the following pairs of words is spelled incorrectly. Circle that word and spell it correctly on the line provided.

1. tornado, pianoes   _____

2. shampooes, studios   _____

3. stereoes, banjos   _____

4. rodeo, portfolioes   _____

5. radioes, heroes   _____

6. banjo, sopranoes   _____

7. volcanos, tomato   _____

8. potatoes, buffalos   _____

B. In each of the following sentences, one word is spelled incorrectly. Find that word. Then spell it correctly on the line provided.

9. The new building will have two dance studioes.   _____

10. I'll be earning extra money picking potatos during vacation.   _____

11. Laura has two banjoes in her collection.   _____

12. Ted and Janet are the heros of the team.   _____

13. There have been many teenage rodeoes in Texas.   _____

14. Don't forget to put some tomatos in the salad.   _____

15. Over the years, tornados have caused great damage to lives and property.   _____

6 Greenpeace

"We've had our people in some very flaky situations. It's a small miracle that no one has gotten killed," says Bob Hunter, speaking for the group called Greenpeace. The group is a body of people who are determined to stop the senseless killing of animals. Sometimes they even risk their own lives to protect wildlife.

Their main work has been in saving whales. Some countries still hunt whales, using large, modern whaling ships. The Greenpeace ships patrol the oceans. When the Greenpeacers find a whale about to be killed by hunters, they go into action. They launch small motor-driven rafts and get between the whales and the hunters. Whale hunters can't fire their harpoons without risking injury to a Greenpeace member. A harpoon is a long spear with a knife-sharp edge. Once, while protecting a mother whale and her calf, the Greenpeacers were fired upon. A harpoon came close to hitting the courageous volunteers.

Lately, things have changed. Whalers want to avoid trouble. They hold their fire when they see a Greenpeace raft. Greenpeace members have even boarded a Russian whaling ship. Instead of arguing, they handed out "Save the Whales" T-shirts to the crew. It seems that Greenpeace is not only saving whales but also making friends!

The group was begun in the late 1960s. A few Canadians and Americans joined together and called themselves the Greenpeace Foundation. Their numbers have grown steadily ever since. Today, they are a multinational organization known as Greenpeace International. Their home base is Lewes, England. They have over 250,000 members from all over the world.

●REVIEWING YOUR READING

Circle the letter beside the word or phrase that best completes the sentence.

1. Greenpeace is a body of people who are determined to save

   a. whaling ships.
   b. whalers.
   c. wildlife.
   d. national parks.

2. The Greenpeace ships

   a. hunt whales.
   b. patrol the oceans.
   c. kill hunters.
   d. were sunk.

3. In trying to save the whales, the Greenpeacers have

   a. captured whales.
   b. captured hunters.
   c. gotten between the whales and their calves.
   d. gotten between the whales and the hunters.

4. A harpoon is a

   a. big whale.
   b. small boat.
   c. long spear.
   d. huge raft.

5. The whalers want to

   a. avoid trouble.
   b. hurt the Greenpeacers.
   c. destroy the Greenpeace ships.
   d. form an organization of their own.

6. Greenpeacers once boarded a Russian ship and handed out

   a. food.
   b. T-shirts.
   c. harpoons.
   d. rafts.

7. The home base for Greenpeace is

   a. Chicago, Illinois.
   b. Mexico City, Mexico.
   c. Lewes, England.
   d. Vancouver, British Columbia.

8. According to the story, you can conclude that Greenpeacers are

   a. not protecting whales.
   b. protecting hunters.
   c. saving whales and making friends.
   d. selling whales to hunters.

• FIGURING THE FACTS

Decide whether the following statements are true or false. Write **T** on the line if the statement is true. If the statement is false, change the statement to make it true. Cross out the incorrect word or phrase in the sentence. Then, if necessary, write the correct word or phrase on the line.

1. Sometimes Greenpeacers risk their own lives to save animals.   _____

2. The main work of Greenpeace is saving lions.   _____

3. Sometimes the Greenpeacers use motor-driven rafts.   _____

4. Greenpeacers often protect mother whales from their calves.   _____

5. Once, an arrow came close to hitting a Greenpeace member.   _____

6. The members of Greenpeace are volunteers.   _____

7. Today, whalers hold their fire when they see a Greenpeace raft.   _____

8. Greenpeace was begun in the late 1930s.   _____

9. The Greenpeace Foundation was started by Canadians and Russians.   _____

10. There are over 250,000 Greenpeace members around the world.   _____

• WHAT'S YOUR OPINION?

1. Would you risk your life to save an animal? Why or why not?

    _____

    _____

    _____

2. Greenpeacers have used dangerous methods such as risking their lives, and peaceful methods like handing out T-shirts. Which do you think is more effective? Why?

    _____

    _____

    _____

●DEVELOPING SPELLING SKILLS

Study List

Singular	Plural
calf	calves
elf	elves
half	halves
hoof	hooves
knife	knives
leaf	leaves
life	lives
loaf	loaves
ourself	ourselves
shelf	shelves
thief	thieves
wharf	wharves
wife	wives
wolf	wolves
yourself	yourselves

Some words ending in *f*, like *sheriff*, form their plurals the regular way—by adding *s*. The plural of *sheriff* is *sheriffs*. However, some words that end in *f* or *fe* form their plurals irregularly.

Rule: *Some words that end in* **f** *or* **fe** *form their plurals by dropping the* **f** *or* **fe** *and adding* **ves**.

Examples:

Singular	Plural
life	*lives*
knife	*knives*
calf	*calves*

On your left is a Study List of words. Each word ends in *f* or *fe* in its singular form. All of these words form their plurals by dropping the final *f* or *fe* and adding *ves*. The words listed are almost all the words in English that form their plurals this way.

● SKILL DRILL 1

Circle the final *f* or *fe* in each of the following words. Then write the plural form of the word on the line provided.

1. thief _____   8. shelf _____

2. ourself _____   9. leaf _____

3. loaf _____   10. calf _____

4. elf _____   11. yourself _____

5. life _____   12. hoof _____

6. wolf _____   13. knife _____

7. half _____   14. wife _____

15. wharf _____

● SKILL DRILL 2

The following are short definitions of words from the Study List. The definitions are for the words in their singular form. Write the *singular form* of the Study List word that matches the definition. If you need help, check the Mini-Dictionary in the back of this book.

1. Bread shaped in one long piece _____

2. A wild animal somewhat like a dog _____

3. One who steals _____

4. A piece of wood that is fastened to a wall to hold things such as books _____

5. A cutting tool with a sharp edge _____

6. One of two equal parts _____

7. A married woman _____

8. A platform for loading and unloading ships _____

9. We or us _____

10. A thin, green part of a tree or plant _____

11. A tiny, mischievous character in fairy tales _____

12. You _____

13. The period of living _____

14. A hard covering on the feet of some animals _____

15. A young cow, bull, whale, or elephant _____

● SKILL DRILL 3

Fill in each blank with the plural of the noun in parentheses to form a Study List word.

1. Please be sure to take care of (yourself) _____ .

2. The calf's (hoof) _____ were stirring up the dust.

3. This bakery will sell (half) _____ of a cake.

4. Many hungry (wolf) _____ are roaming this forest.

5. There are plenty of empty (shelf) _____ in the closet.

6. The sharper (knife) _____ are in the drawer.

7. The workers will unload the ships down at the (wharf) _____ .

8. We always enjoy (ourself) _____ at the picnic.

9. The trees are beginning to lose their (leaf) _____ .

10. There are (elf) _____ living in the stump of that tree.

11. The members risk their (life) _____ to save the whales.

12. Three young (calf) _____ were running across the field.

13. The boys are making (loaf) _____ of bread.

14. People who shoplift are (thief) _____ .

15. All of these women are (wife) _____ and mothers.

● SKILL DRILL 4

Answer the following questions by using words from the Study List. You must write both the singular and plural forms of the word.

Singular	Plural

Which word has the vowel combination *ie* ?

1. _____   _____

Which word has the vowel combination *ea* ?

2. _____   _____

Which words contain the word *elf* in their singular form?

3. _____   _____

4. _____   _____

5. _____   _____

	Singular	**Plural**

6. _____   _____

Which word contains the vowel combination *oa*?

7. _____   _____

Which word contains the vowel combination *oo*?

8. _____   _____

Which words end with *ife* in their singular form?

9. _____   _____

10. _____   _____

11. _____   _____

What word ends with *arf* in its singular form?

12. _____   _____

Which words end with *alf* in their singular form?

13. _____   _____

14. _____   _____

Which word ends with *olf* in its singular form?

15. _____   _____

Study List

Plural
calves
elves
halves
hooves
knives
leaves
lives
loaves
ourselves
shelves
thieves
wharves
wives
wolves
yourselves

● WORD GAME 6

This is a puzzle without clues! Study the length and spelling of the plural form of each Study List word. Then figure out which words from the Study List fit in the spaces. Once you have found the first word, the rest will be easy to find. Remember to use the plural form of each word.

● HOW WELL CAN YOU SPELL?

Try to take this practice test without looking back at Lesson 6. After you have finished, check your work against the Study List. Correct any mistakes you have made.

A. One word in each of the following pairs of words is spelled incorrectly. Circle that word and spell it correctly on the line provided.

1. elves, knifes   _____

2. lifes, yourself   _____

3. calves, wifes   _____

4. half, hoovs   _____

5. woolfs, loaves   _____

6. wharf, ourselfs   _____

7. shelvs, leaves   _____

8. thiefs, knife   _____

B. In each of the following sentences, one word is spelled incorrectly. Find that word. Then spell it correctly on the line provided.

9. Diane divided all of the pieces into halfs.   _____

10. There are several loafs of bread on the shelf.   _____

11. The car is parked down by the wharfs.   _____

12. Tom thinks that he's been seeing elfs.   _____

13. Please treat yourselfs to some milk and cookies. _____

14. The mother whale is protecting her calfs.   _____

15. In summer, those trees are covered with leafs.   _____

7 Riches From the Deep

The year was 1641. Pirates roamed the Caribbean Sea off the coast of South America. Huge galleons, which are Spanish sailing vessels, sailed the seven seas. The Spanish ship, *Concepción*, was heavy with treasure and on its way home. As it came near to the Florida coast, a fierce hurricane rose. The ship was helpless. Desperately, the crew cut loose sails and chopped off pieces of wood that held the sails. They were trying to keep the vessel afloat. But the *Concepción* was overturned.

While still hoping to hide the ship's treasure from the pirates, the captain made way for Puerto Rico. But 80 miles (128 kilometers) from shore, the ship hit a coral reef. Along with its precious cargo, the ship sank to the ocean floor.

Just 44 years later, the treasure was found. William Phips, an adventurer from Maine, was sent by the king of England to discover the remains of the sunken vessel. He hauled up 32 tons of silver from the wreck. Phips gave one fifth of his find to the king of England, who still ruled over America. Phips was then made governor of the Massachusetts Bay Colony.

But that was hardly the end of the *Concepción's* story. Three hundred years after the ship went down, an adventurer named Burt Webber decided to try to find it. Webber searched for a few months and found nothing. He was about to give up. Luckily, before he did, William Phips's record book was found in England. Webber and his crew set sail, closely following the directions in Phips's log. A short distance from where the ship went down, they began to find treasure.

Experts claimed that there might be as much as 40 million dollars worth of gold and silver in the ship's watery grave. "It could go beyond one's wildest dreams," said Webber. It looked like his ship had finally come in!

●REVIEWING YOUR READING

Circle the letter beside the word or phrase that best completes the sentence.

1. The *Concepción* was a

    a. Russian ship.
    b. Spanish ship.
    c. French ship.
    d. British ship.

2. The ship was helpless when it sailed into a

    a. tornado.
    b. snowstorm.
    c. hurricane.
    d. cyclone.

3. The captain of the *Concepción* sailed toward Puerto Rico to

    a. spend the gold.
    b. take a vacation.
    c. sink the ship.
    d. hide the treasure.

4. The *Concepción* sank off the coast of

    a. Puerto Rico.
    b. Spain.
    c. Maine.
    d. Florida.

5. William Phips hauled up 32 tons of

    a. copper.
    b. silver.
    c. tin.
    d. diamonds.

6. Phips gave one fifth of the treasure he found to the

    a. king of England.
    b. governor of Massachusetts.
    c. president of Spain.
    d. governor of Puerto Rico.

7. A captain's log is a

    a. record book.
    b. piece of wood.
    c. huge sail.
    d. galleon.

8. Webber and his crew found the remains of the *Concepción* by

    a. following a treasure map.
    b. following the directions in Phips's log.
    c. digging near Puerto Rico.
    d. asking pirates for directions.

● FIGURING THE FACTS

Decide whether the following statements are true or false. Write **T** on the line if the statement is true. If the statement is false, change the statement to make it true. Cross out the incorrect word or phrase in the sentence. Then, if necessary, write the correct word or phrase on the line.

1. A *galleon* is a treasure.   _____

2. To keep the *Concepción* afloat, the crew cut loose the sails.   _____

3. The *Concepción* sank when it hit another ship.   _____

4. William Phips was an adventurer from Spain.   _____

5. Phips found the treasure two years after the *Concepción* sank.   _____

6. Phips was made a knight by the king of England. _____

7. Phips was made governor of Maine.   _____

8. Three hundred years after the ship went down, Webber tried to find it.   _____

9. Webber finally found treasure near the spot where the *Titanic* sank.   _____

10. There may be as much as 40 million dollars worth of treasure in the *Concepción's* watery grave. _____

● WHAT'S YOUR OPINION?

1. William Phips was sent by the king of England to find the treasure. Do you think that it was worth Phips's while? Why?

_____

_____

_____

2. William Phips's record book helped Webber find the remains of the *Concepción*. Do you think it is important to keep records? Why?

_____

_____

_____

● **DEVELOPING SPELLING SKILLS**

Study List

absolutely
accurately
certainly
cleverly
clumsily
coarsely
desperately
entirely
immediately
luckily
nearly
rapidly
recently
separately
wearily

An **adjective** is a word that describes something. Look at this sentence: The *clever* fox hid behind the tree. The word *clever* is an adjective because it describes the noun *fox*.

An **adverb** is a word that describes the action. Look at this sentence: The fox *cleverly* hid behind the tree. The word *cleverly* is an adverb because it describes how the fox hid.

Notice that the difference in spelling between the adjective *clever* and the adverb *cleverly* is the suffix *ly*.

Rule: *To change most adjectives to adverbs, simply add the suffix* **ly**.

Here are some adjectives and adverbs taken from the reading selection.

Examples:

Adjectives	Adverbs
near	nearly
clever	cleverly
desperate	desperately
lucky	luckily

Notice that all the adjectives simply add *ly* to form adverbs—except *lucky*. Do you remember why? The rule for words that end in *y* applies to this word. Here is the rule to refresh your memory.

Rule: *When a word ends in* **y** *preceded by a consonant, change the* **y** *to* **i** *before adding a suffix except* **ing**.

On your left is a Study List of words. Each word in the list is an adverb.

● SKILL DRILL 1

Change each of the following adjectives to adverbs by adding the suffix *ly*. Be sure to remember the rule for adding suffixes to words that end with the letter *y*.

1. clever _____
2. entire _____
3. accurate _____
4. clumsy _____
5. weary _____
6. certain _____
7. near _____

8. recent _____
9. immediate _____
10. coarse _____
11. desperate _____
12. absolute _____
13. lucky _____
14. separate _____

15. rapid _____

● SKILL DRILL 2

The following are short definitions of words from the Study List. Fill the blanks with words from the Study List that match the definitions. If you need help, check the Mini-Dictionary in the back of this book.

1. Without any restrictions; completely _____
2. Including all the parts _____
3. Without delay; happening at once _____
4. In a tired or worn-out way _____
5. Divided into parts or groups; individually _____
6. Having a good result by chance _____
7. Almost; not quite _____
8. Very swiftly or quickly _____
9. Happening a short time ago _____
10. In an awkward manner _____
11. Correctly _____
12. Quick in thinking; smart _____
13. Without any doubt or question _____
14. Roughly; harshly _____
15. Reckless because one has lost hope _____

● SKILL DRILL 3

Fill in each blank with the adverb form of the adjective in parentheses to form a Study List word.

Study List

absolutely
accurately
certainly
cleverly
clumsily
coarsely
desperately
entirely
immediately
luckily
nearly
rapidly
recently
separately
wearily

1. The hikers (desperate) _____ climbed to the top.

2. Please come to my office (immediate) _____ .

3. (Lucky) _____ , there was a police officer nearby.

4. The fire destroyed (near) _____ all the trees.

5. The stream is moving quite (rapid) _____ .

6. We all went to the movies (recent) _____ .

7. Please wash those glasses (separate) _____ .

8. The workers (weary) _____ marched toward home.

9. She is (absolute) _____ the best tennis player here.

10. Add two cups of onions (coarse) _____ chopped.

11. There is (certain) _____ no doubt of his ability.

12. The fox (clever) _____ hid behind the trees.

13. Please be sure you have added the figures (accurate) _____ .

14. The ship is made (entire) _____ of wood.

15. The clown (clumsy) _____ fell into the barrel.

● SKILL DRILL 4

Answer the following questions by using words from the Study List.

Which words contain the word *ate* ?

1. _____   2. _____

3. _____   4. _____

Which word contains the word *oar* ?

5. _____

Which words contain the word *ear* ?

6. _____   7. _____

Which word contains the word *lute* ?

8. _____

Which word ends with the letters *sily* ?

9. _____

Which word contains the work *luck* ?

10. _____

Which word contains the word *rapid* ?

11. _____

Which word contains the word *certain* ?

12. _____

Which word contains the word *cent* ?

13. _____

Which word contains the word *tire* ?

14. _____

Which word contains the word *ever* ?

15. _____

● WORD GAME 7

The words from the Study List are scrambled on the left. Unscramble each word and write it correctly in the spaces on the right. If you unscramble the words correctly, you will find the answer to the puzzle question by reading the shaded column downward. Write your answer on the line below.

P A D R I L Y

S E D R E A P E T L Y
L O S B A E T U L Y
R A T E N C I L Y
C I K L U L Y
L E C E V R L Y
T R N E C E L Y

R I T E E N L Y
R E A N L Y
P E A S R T A E L Y
I W A E R L Y
R O E S A C L Y
S I M C U L L Y
U C A C A R E T L Y
M I M I D E T A E L Y

What do you call riches from the deep? _____

●HOW WELL CAN YOU SPELL?

Try to take this practice test without looking back at Lesson 7. After you have finished, check your work against the Study List. Correct any mistakes you have made.

A. One word in each of the following pairs of words is spelled incorrectly. Circle that word and spell it correctly on the line provided.

1. certainlly, cleverly   _____

2. entirely, rapidley   _____

3. recently, luckly   _____

4. coarsly, clumsily   _____

5. absolutely, separatelly   _____

6. accuratly, nearly   _____

7. immediatelly, wearily   _____

8. luckily, desperatly   _____

B. In each of the following sentences, one word is spelled incorrectly. Find that word. Then spell it correctly on the line provided.

9. We recentley visited the Museum of Modern Art.   _____

10. Edgar clumsyly tripped over the carpet.   _____

11. Your answer is absolutly correct.   _____

12. The dog cleverley hid the bone in the yard.   _____

13. That shirt is made entireley of silk.   _____

14. There aren't nearley enough people present.   _____

15. The shoppers came weariley home from the market.   _____

8 A Star Reborn

In her youth she was one of America's finest jazz singers. She dropped out of show business for over 20 years, and then made a comeback. She has written songs and made recordings. She has even been a nurse. No matter how old she was, age never stopped Alberta Hunter.

At the age of 11, Alberta Hunter ran away from her Memphis, Tennessee, home. She had learned that young people could get jobs singing in Chicago. Wandering north to the strange city, she found a job peeling potatoes, through a friend. The pay was $6.00 a week, plus room and board. But Alberta really wanted to find a job singing. So each night when everyone was asleep, she went out and looked for a job as a singer. Of course she was too young, but that didn't stop her. One lucky night, she got her chance. She belted out her songs in a shabby nightclub. The audience loved her. From then on, her career flowed as freely as her music. Alberta Hunter's musical career lasted more than 50 years!

In 1957, Alberta's mother died. They had always been very close. The death made Alberta question her own life. "I wanted to do something for humanity," she said. Soon after her mother's funeral, she enrolled in nursing school. She was 62, but she told the teachers at the school that she was 50. Before long she was caring for patients at a New York City hospital. After 20 years of nursing, Alberta was asked to retire because of her age. The hospital thought she was 70. She was really 82!

But retirement only meant rediscovery for Alberta Hunter. At age 83, she decided to go back to singing. At a party for a friend, she entertained the guests with a song. From then on she was back in show business, singing in clubs, on TV, even in movies. Alberta Hunter was determined to follow the lyrics of one of her songs—"Tomorrow I may die, and I ain't passin' nothin' by!"

● REVIEWING YOUR READING

Circle the letter beside the word or phrase that best completes the sentence.

1. For 20 years, Alberta Hunter worked as a

   a. doctor.
   b. nurse.
   c. teacher.
   d. potato peeler.

2. At age 11, she ran away to

   a. Memphis.
   b. Chicago.
   c. Europe.
   d. Atlanta.

3. Her first job in Chicago was

   a. driving a bus.
   b. singing songs.
   c. peeling potatoes.
   d. cooking food.

4. Alberta Hunter looked for work as a singer when everyone was

   a. asleep.
   b. eating lunch.
   c. eating breakfast.
   d. away from home.

5. She became a nurse after her

   a. graduation from high school.
   b. mother's death.
   c. graduation from college.
   d. sister's death.

6. Alberta Hunter told the teachers at the school that she was

   a. 75.
   b. 83.
   c. 62.
   d. 50.

7. She worked as a nurse in

   a. Chicago.
   b. Memphis.
   c. New York.
   d. Atlanta.

8. According to the story, you can conclude that Alberta Hunter began her return to singing

   a. in Chicago.
   b. in Europe.
   c. at a friend's party.
   d. at a hospital.

● FIGURING THE FACTS

Decide whether the following statements are true or false. Write **T** on the line if the statement is true. If the statement is false, change the statement to make it true. Cross out the incorrect word or phrase in the sentence. Then, if necessary, write the correct word or phrase on the line.

1. Alberta Hunter made her singing comeback at age 33. _____

2. At age 11, she heard that young people could get jobs singing in Chicago. _____

3. Her first job in Chicago was singing. _____

4. She got her first chance to sing in a shabby nightclub. _____

5. Alberta Hunter's singing career lasted 15 years. _____

6. She and her mother had a close relationship. _____

7. She enrolled in nursing school before her mother's death. _____

8. The death of her mother forced Alberta Hunter to question her own life. _____

9. Alberta Hunter was asked to retire from nursing because of her age. _____

10. After her retirement, Alberta Hunter never sang again. _____

● WHAT'S YOUR OPINION?

1. What do you think Alberta Hunter meant when she said, "I wanted to do something for humanity"?

_____

_____

_____

2. How do you think the lyrics, "Tomorrow I may die, and I ain't passin' nothin' by," relate to the way Alberta Hunter lives her life?

_____

_____

_____

● DEVELOPING SPELLING SKILLS

**Study
List**

accidentally
actually
cheerfully
faithfully
finally
gracefully
initially
legally
locally
naturally
occasionally
practically
really
respectfully
totally

As you know, an **adjective** is a word that describes something. Look at this sentence: *Graceful* Alberta Hunter sang a tune. The word *graceful* is an adjective because it describes the noun *Alberta Hunter*.

An **adverb** is a word that describes the action. Look at this sentence: Alberta Hunter *gracefully* sang a tune. The word *gracefully* describes how she sang the tune.

Notice that the difference between the adjective *graceful* and the adverb *gracefully* is the suffix *ly*.

Rule: *To change adjectives that end in* **l** *to adverbs, add the suffix* **ly.**

Examples:

Adjectives	**Adverbs**
accidental	accidentally
real	really
graceful	gracefully

On your left is a Study List of words. Each word in the list is an adverb.

● SKILL DRILL 1

Change the following adjectives to adverbs by adding the suffix *ly*.

1. respectful _____   8. total _____

2. accidental _____   9. natural _____

3. occasional _____   10. practical _____

4. real _____   11. actual _____

5. cheerful _____   12. faithful _____

6. final _____   13. graceful _____

7. initial _____   14. legal _____

15. local _____

● SKILL DRILL 2

The following are short definitions of words from the Study List. Fill the blanks with words from the Study List that match the definitions. If you need help, check the Mini-Dictionary in the back of this book.

1. Almost or nearly _____

2. Truly or actually _____

3. Really or in fact _____

4. Done with joy or gladness _____

5. Loyally; honestly _____

6. Last; coming at the end _____

7. First; coming at the beginning _____

8. Beautifully and smoothly _____

9. Allowed by law; lawfully _____

10. Feeling or showing respect _____

11. Completely; entirely; in a total manner _____

12. Mistakenly; unexpectedly; happening by mistake _____

13. In a natural way; as one might expect _____

14. Once in awhile; now and then _____

15. Within a particular place; nearby _____

● SKILL DRILL 3

Answer the following questions by using words from the Study List.

Which word contains the word *tot*?

1. _____

Which word contains the word *occasion*?

2. _____

Which word contains the word *accident*?

3. _____

Which words contain the word *act*?

4. _____   5. _____

Which words contain the word *fully*?

6. _____   7. _____

8. _____   9. _____

Which word contains the word *leg*?

10. _____

Which word contains the word *real*?

11. _____

Study List

accidentally
actually
cheerfully
faithfully
finally
gracefully
initially
legally
locally
naturally
occasionally
practically
really
respectfully
totally

Which word contains the word *natural*?   Which word contains the word *fin*?

12. _____   13. _____

Which word contains the word *local*?   Which word contains the word *initial*?

14. _____   15. _____

● SKILL DRILL 4

Fill in each blank with the adverb form of the adjective in parentheses to form a Study List word.

1. The storm did damage (local) _____ .

2. We (occasional) _____ go to that restaurant.

3. All of these vegetables are grown (natural) _____ .

4. James (accidental) _____ broke the mirror.

5. Alberta Hunter was not (total) _____ truthful about her age.

6. The gentleman (respectful) _____ took off his hat.

7. Please cross the street (legal) _____ .

8. The dancers (graceful) _____ waltzed across the floor.

9. The letter (final) _____ arrived today.

10. My alarm clock rings (faithful) _____ at eight.

11. The children (cheerful) _____ greeted the ambassador.

12. Jane is (real) _____ leaving this afternoon.

13. That picture was (initial) _____ at the front of the book.

14. There is (practical) _____ no mustard left.

15. She is (actual) _____ Margo's twin sister.

● WORD GAME 8

The words in the Study List are used in this puzzle. The numbers of the clues match the numbers in the puzzle. Read the clues below. Then write your answers in the puzzle blocks.

ACROSS
4. Synonym for *really*
6. At the beginning
7. In a total manner
10. Coming at the end
12. In a natural way
13. Nearby
14. Synonym for *actually*
15. Showing respect

DOWN
1. Loyally; deserving trust
2. By mistake
3. Almost or nearly
5. Done with joy
8. Once in awhile
9. Having grace or beauty
11. Allowed by law

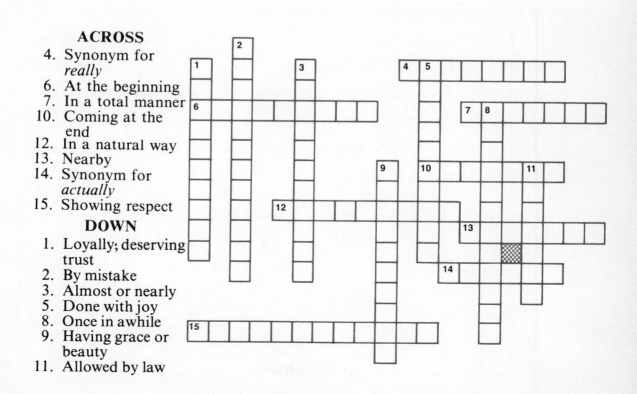

● HOW WELL CAN YOU SPELL?

Try to take this practice test without looking back at Lesson 8. After you have finished, check your work against the Study List. Correct any mistakes you have made.

A. One word in each of the following pairs of words is spelled incorrectly. Circle that word and spell it correctly on the line provided.

1. faithfuly, finally   _____

2. really, localy   _____

3. totaly, gracefully   _____

4. initialy, cheerfully   _____

5. actually, legaly   _____

6. occasionally, naturaly   _____

7. respectfuly, accidentally _____

B. In each of the following sentences, one word is spelled incorrectly. Find that word. Then spell it correctly on the line provided.

8. Ellen is actualy the first person on the list.   _____

9. The family occasionaly goes to the park together.   _____

10. We accidentaly took the wrong turn.   _____

11. He arrived when dinner was practicaly over.   _____

12. Finaly, the train slowly approached the station.   _____

13. This is realy the first time I've been on skates.   _____

14. Dorothy gracefuly turned on the ice.   _____

15. Mr. Johnson cheerfuly greets his students each morning. _____

9 The Dinner Party

It took almost five years to set the table. But the "guests" will never sit down to eat because it's not a real dinner party. It's a work of art. The creation is a combination of sculpture, painting, and needlework. It is called "The Dinner Party," and it is dedicated to all the women of the world.

"The Dinner Party" stands in the center of a room at San Francisco's Museum of Modern Art. The main piece is a huge, triangular-shaped table. This object was chosen partly because the triangle has been a symbol for women throughout history. Also, in the past, women have been known as preparers of the family table.

There are 39 settings of silverware and china. Each place is for a famous woman in history. Each has a different handmade plate, tableware, and a drinking goblet. At each place is a linen mat on which the famous woman's name is sewn. Also hand-stitched on the mat are some pictures and symbols that show the life of the famous "guest."

The huge table rests on a floor made of triangular clay tiles. Nine hundred and ninety-nine women's names are written on these tiles. All of the names are important in world history.

The project was the idea of artist Judy Chicago. For the first two years, Judy worked alone on the creation. Slowly, others grew interested and began to offer their help. More than 400 people worked on the masterpiece, which took almost five years to complete. Their work is a celebration of women in art and history. And there couldn't be a better place to celebrate than at a dinner party!

● **REVIEWING YOUR READING**

Circle the letter beside the word or phrase that best completes the sentence.

1. "The Dinner Party" is a

   a. picture.
   b. piece of music.
   c. work of art.
   d. meal.

2. "The Dinner Party" is dedicated to all the

   a. people of the world.
   b. women of the world.
   c. men of the world.
   d. children of the world.

3. The main piece in "The Dinner Party" is a

   a. square table.
   b. round table.
   c. triangular-shaped table.
   d. rectangular-shaped table.

4. At the table there are

   a. 39 people.
   b. 39 place settings.
   c. 93 people.
   d. 93 place settings.

5. The triangle is an ancient symbol for

   a. women.
   b. art.
   c. dinner.
   d. sculpture.

6. Each place setting has a hand-stitched

   a. plate.
   b. knife.
   c. mat.
   d. napkin.

7. The word *stitched* means

   a. drawn.
   b. sewn.
   c. painted.
   d. cooked.

8. For the first two years, Judy Chicago worked on "The Dinner Party"

   a. alone.
   b. with 88 other people.
   c. only at night.
   d. with 3 other people.

● FIGURING THE FACTS

Decide whether the following statements are true or false. Write **T** on the line if the statement is true. If the statement is false, change the statement to make it true. Cross out the incorrect word or phrase in the sentence. Then, if necessary, write the correct word or phrase on the line.

1. It took almost ten years to create "The Dinner Party." _____

2. "The Dinner Party" is a combination of sculpture, needlework, and music. _____

3. "The Dinner Party" celebrates women in history. _____

4. In the past, women have been known as preparers of the table. _____

5. Each setting at the table is dedicated to a real woman in history. _____

6. The plates on the table were made by hand. _____

7. There is a plastic mat at each place on the table. _____

8. A drinking goblet is a type of a cup. _____

9. The table rests on a floor made of clay tiles. _____

10. The tiles are in the shape of squares. _____

● WHAT'S YOUR OPINION?

1. In the past, women have been known as preparers of the table. Why do you think this was the case? How have things changed?

_____

_____

_____

2. In what ways is the table of "The Dinner Party" different from other dinner tables? What do you think makes Judy Chicago's table a work of art?

_____

_____

_____

● **DEVELOPING SPELLING SKILLS**

Study List

artist's
couldn't
doesn't
haven't
it's
mechanic's
passenger's
secretary's
shouldn't
we'll
where's
women's
won't
wouldn't
you've

There are two major uses of the **apostrophe** that you should know.

Rule: *The apostrophe is used to show possession.*

Example: The artist's painting

The painting is owned by the artist. Therefore, we use the apostrophe followed by the letter *s* to show possession.

Example: Women's names

The names belong to the *women*. Therefore, we again use the apostrophe followed by the letter *s* to show possession.

Rule: *The apostrophe is used to show that a letter or letters have been omitted.*

Example: **Couldn't** is a short form of **could not.**

Could and *not* have been joined together and the second *o* has been omitted. The place for the missing letter is being held by the apostrophe.

Example: **Won't** is a short form of **will not.**

Will and *not* have been joined together and the space for the missing letters is held open by the apostrophe.

Words like *couldn't* and *won't* are called **contractions** because they shorten or contract two words.

On your left is a Study List of words. Each demonstrates a use of the apostrophe. Remember, there are two major uses of the apostrophe: to show possession or to replace a missing letter.

● SKILL DRILL 1

Each of the following words is missing an apostrophe. Rewrite each word with the apostrophe in its proper place.

1. shouldnt _____   8. couldnt _____

2. secretarys _____   9. doesnt _____

3. its _____   10. mechanics _____

4. passengers _____   11. artists _____

5. wouldnt _____   12. wont _____

6. womens _____   13. havent _____

7. wheres _____   14. well _____

15. youve _____

● SKILL DRILL 2

The following are short definitions of words from the Study List. Fill the blanks with words from the Study List that match the definitions. If you need help, check the Mini-Dictionary in the back of this book.

1. Belonging to the mechanic _____

2. Belonging to the passenger _____

3. Could not _____

4. Have not _____

5. Belonging to the artist _____

6. Will not _____

7. Belonging to the women _____

8. Should not _____

9. Belonging to the secretary _____

10. Does not _____

11. It is _____

12. Would not _____

13. Where is _____

14. We will _____

15. You have _____

● **SKILL DRILL 3**

Change the words in parentheses to possessives or contractions and rewrite the sentence on the line provided. The first one is done for you.

1. The studio (of the artist) contains many beautiful paintings.

The artist's studio contains many beautiful paintings.

2. The tools (of the mechanic) are in the bag.

_____

3. Tom (could not) attend the class picnic.

_____

4. The luggage (of the passenger) is on the train.

_____

5. I (have not) been to the library for two days.

_____

6. Sandra (will not) be taking the bus today.

_____

7. The paintings (of the women) will be on display tonight.

_____

8. A person (should not) go swimming after eating a big meal.

_____

9. The desk (of the secretary) is in the corner.

_____

10. The whole trip (does not) take more than three hours.

_____

11. (It is) ten minutes past four o'clock.

_____

12. (You have) stored plenty of food in the refrigerator.

_____

13. I (would not) do that if I were you.

_____

14. (Where is) the vacuum cleaner?

_____

15. We're going away, but (we will) be right back.

_____

● SKILL DRILL 4

Answer the following questions by using words from the Study List.

Which words are possessives?

1. _____   2. _____

3. _____   4. _____

5. _____

Which contractions contain an apostrophe in place of the letter *i*?

6. _____   7. _____

Which contraction contains an apostrophe in place of the letters *wi*?

8. _____

Which contractions contain an apostrophe in place of the letter *o*?

9. _____   10. _____

11. _____   12. _____

13. _____   14. _____

Which contraction contains an apostrophe in place of the letters *ha*?

15. _____

Study List

artist's
couldn't
doesn't
haven't
it's
mechanic's
passenger's
secretary's
shouldn't
we'll
where's
women's
won't
wouldn't
you've

● WORD GAME 9

All of the letters from the words in the Study List appear in this puzzle. Cross out the letters of the puzzle as you use them to spell the Study List words. There will be enough letters left to answer the question below.

What was missing at the "Dinner Party"? _____

● HOW WELL CAN YOU SPELL?

Try to take this practice test without looking back at Lesson 9. After you have finished, check your work against the Study List. Correct any mistakes you have made.

A. One word in each of the following pairs of words is spelled incorrectly. Circle that word and spell it correctly on the line provided. Be careful: a word is spelled incorrectly if an apostrophe is missing or out of place.

1. coul'dnt, wouldn't   _____

2. doe'snt, artist's   _____

3. secretary's, wel'l   _____

4. shoul'dnt, women's   _____

5. passenger's, hav'nt   _____

6. yo've, mechanic's   _____

7. i'ts, won't   _____

B. In each of the following sentences, one word is spelled incorrectly. Find that word. Then spell it correctly on the line provided.

8. There is a flat tire on the mechanics truck.   _____

9. We wont be taking the train to work today.   _____

10. Wheres the flower pot that was on the shelf?   _____

11. Diane will be playing on the womens team.   _____

12. The secretarys note pad is sitting on the desk.   _____

13. The painting is displayed in the artists studio.   _____

14. Please take that passenge'rs ticket.   _____

15. The extra dishes woul'dnt fit into the cupboard.   _____

10 The Flower

His name means "the flower." But it's his career that's blooming. He is easily Canada's best-known athlete. Superior skating and tricky plays are his trade marks. Their effect is spellbinding. If the other hockey team looks confused, Guy LaFleur is on the ice!

"I like controlling the puck," says LaFleur, star of the Montreal Canadiens. But mostly he enjoys upsetting his opponents. He keeps them guessing. Guy has a knack for making the other team look foolish. No one is ever sure just what his next move will be. LaFleur's style pays off. For several years, he scored more points than any other player in the National Hockey League.

Guy began playing hockey seriously at age 13. He started as a member of a junior team in Quebec City, Canada. Soon, he became the highest scoring player in the history of the Quebec Junior League. Today he is a Canadian hero. Crowds mob him everywhere he goes.

But the rewards of success have not come without a high price. Guy's time with his family is very limited. He spends over 100 days a year traveling to other cities that have professional hockey teams. And when he's home, he brings his fame with him. Even a simple shopping trip with his son may turn into a flight from autograph seekers. "It's been like this since I was 17," says Guy. "But the life is nice in other ways. I wouldn't change it for anything."

What are Guy's plans for the future? Of course, there's hockey. But Guy also loves to write. He has written poetry, and someday hopes to complete his autobiography. It seems that Guy LaFleur will continue to grow.

● **REVIEWING YOUR READING**

Circle the letter beside the word or phrase that best completes the sentence.

1. The name *LaFleur* means the

   a. player.
   b. flower.
   c. ice.
   d. star.

2. Guy LaFleur began playing hockey seriously at age

   a. 5.
   b. 23.
   c. 10.
   d. 13.

3. The first team Guy played on was a

   a. junior team.
   b. senior team.
   c. professional team.
   d. National Hockey League team.

4. Guy spends over 100 days a year

   a. teaching.
   b. coaching.
   c. writing.
   d. traveling.

5. Guy was the highest scoring player in the history of the

   a. world.
   b. Russian Hockey League.
   c. Quebec Junior League.
   d. French Hockey League.

6. According to the story, you can conclude that what Guy most enjoys is

   a. signing autographs.
   b. traveling to other cities.
   c. teaching other players.
   d. upsetting his opponents.

7. In the future, Guy hopes to complete

   a. a short story.
   b. a book of poetry.
   c. his autobiography.
   d. a novel.

8. According to the story, you can conclude that Guy

   a. doesn't like the fame.
   b. enjoys his active life.
   c. is not used to his active life.
   d. does not want his son to play hockey.

● FIGURING THE FACTS

Decide whether the following statements are true or false. Write **T** on the line if the statement is true. If the statement is false, change the statement to make it true. Cross out the incorrect word or phrase in the sentence. Then, if necessary, write the correct word or phrase on the line.

1. Guy LaFleur is Canada's best-known athlete. _____

2. Guy is known for his tricky plays. _____

3. Guy has a knack for making the other team look foolish. _____

4. For several years, Guy scored more points than any other player in the National Hockey League. _____

5. Guy first played on a junior team in Boston. _____

6. Guy spends most of his time with his family. _____

7. Crowds mob Guy everywhere he goes. _____

8. There are many things about his life that Guy would change. _____

9. Guy will someday write a book about his life. _____

10. Guy plays for the Boston Bruins. _____

● WHAT'S YOUR OPINION?

1. Guy is always being mobbed by autograph seekers, but he doesn't seem to mind. How would you feel if people were always after you to sign autographs? Why?

_____

_____

_____

_____

2. Guy doesn't get to spend much time with his family. Do you think it is important for a parent to spend time with his or her family? Why?

_____

_____

_____

_____

● **DEVELOPING SPELLING SKILLS**

Study List

The following words appear in the reading selection.

autobiography   superior   guessing

Each of these words contains two vowels together. We don't always hear all of the sounds in words. Sometimes the vowels come together to make one sound like the *au* in *autobiography*. But notice that the *i* and *o* in autobiography are sounded separately. Therefore, it is most important to know how to spell words with compound vowels like those above.

associate
autobiography
avoid
biscuit
bouquet
career
committee
essential
guessing
optional
pursuit
recruit
superior
theater
understood

On your left is a Study List of words. Each of these words contains two vowels in combination with each other. Be extra careful when spelling these words.

● SKILL DRILL 1

Rewrite each of the following words on the lines provided. Then circle the vowel combinations in each.

1. bouquet _____   8. career _____

2. optional _____   9. pursuit _____

3. recruit _____   10. superior _____

4. theater _____   11. understood _____

5. associate _____   12. autobiography _____

6. avoid _____   13. biscuit _____

7. committee _____   14. essential _____

15. guessing _____

● SKILL DRILL 2

The following are short definitions of words from the Study List. Fill the blanks with words from the Study List that match the definitions. If you need help, check the Mini-Dictionary in the back of this book.

1. Forming an opinion without really knowing _____

2. A bunch of flowers _____

3. A place where plays are acted _____

4. Necessary; needed to make a thing what it is _____

5. To have learned the meaning of something _____

6. To join or connect with something _____

7. The story of a person's life written by him or her _____

8. To keep away from _____

9. A job or course of progress through life _____

10. Not required; left to one's own choice _____

11. The act of pursuing or following _____

12. To get new members _____

13. Very good or above average _____

14. A group of persons appointed to do certain things _____

15. A small, soft bread-like cake _____

● SKILL DRILL 3

The vowels are missing from each of the following words. First, fill the blanks with vowels to form words from the Study List. Then write the words you have formed on the lines provided.

1. und _ rst _ _ d   _____

2. _ ss _ c _ _ t _   _____

3. c _ r _ _ r   _____

4. _ pt _ _ n _ l   _____

5. p _ rs _ _ t   _____

6. _ ss _ nt _ _ l   _____

7. _ _ t _ b _ _ gr _ phy   _____

8. _ v _ _ d   _____

9. g _ _ ss _ ng   _____

10. b _ _ q _ _ t   _____

11. th _ _ t _ r   _____

12. r _ cr _ _ t   _____

13. s _ p _ r _ _ r   _____

14. c _ mm _ tt _ _   _____

15. b _ sc _ _ t   _____

Study List

associate
autobiography
avoid
biscuit
bouquet
career
committee
essential
guessing
optional
pursuit
recruit
superior
theater
understood

● SKILL DRILL 4

Answer the following questions by using words from the Study List.

Which words contain the vowel combination *ee*?

1. _____   2. _____

Which word contains the combination *oo*?

3. _____

Which words contain the vowel combination *io*?

4. _____   5. _____

6. _____

Which word contains the vowel combination *oi*?

7. _____

Which words contain the vowel combination *ia*?

8. _____   9. _____

Which word contains the vowel combination *ea*?

10. _____

Which words contain the vowel combination *ui*?

11. _____   12. _____

13. _____

Which words contain the vowel combination *ue*?

14. _____   15. _____

●WORD GAME 10

The words from the Study List are hidden in this puzzle. They read from top to bottom, left to right, and diagonally. Circle the words you find. Make sure they are spelled correctly. When you find a word, cross it off the list.

A	U	T	O	B	I	R	G	R	A	P	H	Y	P	U	R
R	U	B	O	U	Q	U	E	T	C	D	E	A	O	P	S
P	E	T	I	G	T	X	M	C	F	G	H	U	T	I	U
U	H	O	O	S	A	H	N	M	R	K	L	T	A	O	N
R	T	E	G	B	C	Y	E	O	Y	U	Z	O	S	N	D
S	A	L	C	T	I	U	H	A	W	T	I	B	S	A	E
U	O	G	C	O	M	M	I	T	T	E	E	T	O	L	O
I	G	E	T	A	M	P	O	T	P	E	U	O	C	T	C
T	U	R	H	E	R	M	I	G	R	A	R	R	I	R	I
C	E	E	E	S	S	E	N	T	I	A	L	R	A	P	A
A	S	C	N	C	F	O	E	T	T	E	E	A	T	S	T
R	S	U	P	E	R	I	O	R	U	M	P	P	E	K	E
E	I	U	A	V	O	U	N	D	E	R	S	T	O	O	D
A	N	I	S	A	V	O	I	D	R	C	Y	I	Z	C	L
R	G	R	S	U	I	O	P	T	I	O	N	A	L	K	N
P	U	A	U	T	O	B	I	O	G	R	A	P	H	Y	O

● HOW WELL CAN YOU SPELL?

Try to take this practice test without looking back at Lesson 10. After you have finished, check your work against the Study List. Correct any mistakes you have made.

A. One word in each of the following pairs of words is spelled incorrectly. Circle that word and spell it correctly on the line provided.

1. understod, guessing   _____

2. bouquet, avoyd   _____

3. comittie, pursuit   _____

4. recruit, carear   _____

5. superrear, biscuit   _____

6. essential, autobiagraphy   _____

7. optshunal, associate   _____

B. In each of the following sentences, one word is spelled incorrectly. Find that word. Then spell it correctly on the line provided.

8. The play will be performed in the school theeter.   _____

9. The army would like to recroot more women.   _____

10. Be sure to try a biskit with your meal.   _____

11. Brushing is essenchal to good dental care.   _____

12. The older students will not assoseate with club members.   _____

13. Gessing the answers will not help you to pass the test.   _____

14. The winner was presented with a boquet of roses.   _____

15. Everyone is entitled to life, liberty, and the persoot of happiness.   _____

11 Ships of the Desert

Some are seven or eight feet (2.1 or 2.4 meters) tall. They weigh as much as half a ton. They are humpbacked, knock-kneed, and flat-footed. They'll eat almost anything, even bushes, thorns, and leaves. In a moment of hunger, they've been known to eat the straw roof off a desert hut! People may chuckle at these awkward creatures. But camels always have the last laugh.

For people who live in desert areas, camels are the most valuable animals in the world. They are a serious means of transportation. In fact, they are called "ships of the desert." It is a well-earned name. Camels can travel for two or three days without water. When they do drink, they gulp down as much as a bathtub full of water. They are also able to carry up to twice their own weight. And, camels don't get stuck in the sand like cars and trucks do. Best of all, they don't use gasoline!

When it comes to riding, camels are not always eager to cooperate. First you must get the camel to kneel. Then you approach from the rear and scramble aboard, before the camel starts to rise. Once on, the trick is to stay on. When the camel moves, the rider bobs from side to side, and up and down. As in riding a roller coaster, the secret is to hold on tight.

Countless lives have been saved by the strength and endurance of camels. Recently, there was a drought in Central Africa. Thousands of people were in danger of starving. Camels saved the day. They transported 5,000 tons of food through the desert to the helpless people.

But camels aren't used only for transportation. Each year in Saudi Arabia, thousands of people flock to watch the camel races. The sight is something to behold. One hundred camels gallop across the desert, as riders gracefully balance themselves on the humps!

● REVIEWING YOUR READING

Circle the letter beside the word or phrase that best completes the sentence.

1. Camels have been known to eat

    a. tin roofs.
    b. straw roofs.
    c. brick buildings.
    d. glass.

2. In desert countries, camels are called

    a. ships of the desert.
    b. ships of the sea.
    c. trucks of the desert.
    d. horses of the desert.

3. Camels can travel without water for

    a. 2 or 3 days.
    b. 5 or 6 days.
    c. 7 or 8 days.
    d. 9 or 10 days.

4. In order to ride a camel, first you must

    a. get the animal to sit.
    b. get the animal to kneel.
    c. make the animal gallop.
    d. make the animal trot.

5. According to the story, you can conclude that riding a camel is

    a. safe.
    b. smooth.
    c. difficult.
    d. easy.

6. Other than transportation, camels are used for

    a. racing.
    b. food.
    c. digging sand.
    d. finding water.

7. During a drought in Central Africa, camels transported 5,000

    a. tons of food.
    b. tons of water.
    c. people.
    d. desert huts.

8. According to the story, you can conclude that in desert nations camels

    a. are not needed.
    b. do more harm than good.
    c. often get stuck in sand.
    d. are very valuable.

● FIGURING THE FACTS

Decide whether the following statements are true or false. Write **T** on the line if the statement is true. If the statement is false, change the statement to make it true. Cross out the incorrect word or phrase in the sentence. Then, if necessary, write the correct word or phrase on the line.

1. Some camels are seven or eight feet (2.1 or 2.4 meters) tall. _____

2. Some camels weigh as much as eight tons. _____

3. Camels will eat almost anything. _____

4. Camels are not a means of transportation. _____

5. Camels won't drink more than a cup of water at a time. _____

6. Camels can carry up to six times their own weight. _____

7. Camels get stuck in sand. _____

8. Camels are always eager to carry riders. _____

9. A camel rider bobs up and down, and from side to side. _____

10. In Saudi Arabia, there are camel races. _____

● WHAT'S YOUR OPINION?

1. Do you think camels could be a means of transportation where you live? Why or why not?

_____

_____

_____

_____

2. The reading selection tells us that "camels always have the last laugh." What do you think the author means by this?

_____

_____

_____

_____

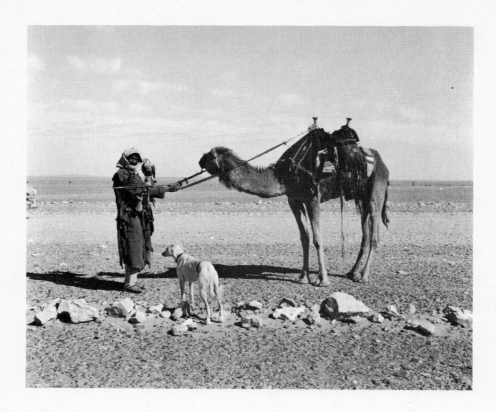

● DEVELOPING SPELLING SKILLS

Study List

The following words appear in the reading selection.

approach   serious   cooperate

Each of these words has two or more vowels together. Since we don't always hear all the sounds in words, it is most important to know how to spell words with multiple vowels like those above. As you read through the Study List words, notice the silent vowels in each word.

On your left is a Study List of words. Each of these words contains two or more vowels in combination with each other. Be extra careful when spelling these words.

ambitious
approach
caution
cooperate
counterfeit
individual
lieutenant
manual
nervous
proclaim
realize
reliable
serious
vacuum
valuable

● **SKILL DRILL 1**

Rewrite each of the following words on the lines provided. Then circle the multiple vowels in each.

1. serious _____
2. valuable _____
3. realize _____
4. nervous _____
5. ambitious _____
6. cooperate _____
7. counterfeit _____

8. vacuum _____
9. reliable _____
10. proclaim _____
11. manual _____
12. approach _____
13. caution _____
14. individual _____

15. lieutenant _____

● **SKILL DRILL 2**

The following are short definitions of words from the Study List. Fill the blanks with words from the Study List that match the definitions. If you need help, check the Mini-Dictionary in the back of this book.

1. An empty space without any air in it _____
2. Showing a strong desire for fame or honor _____
3. To come near or nearer something _____
4. To warn or advise _____
5. Declare or make known publicly _____
6. To understand clearly _____
7. Dependable; worthy of trust _____
8. Important; grave _____
9. An army officer _____
10. Done with the hands _____
11. Restless or uneasy _____
12. Unite and work together _____
13. Not real; an illegal copy _____
14. One single person _____
15. Having value; being worth something _____

● SKILL DRILL 3

The vowels are missing from each of the following words. First, fill the blanks with vowels to form words from the Study List. Then write the words you have formed on the lines provided.

Study List

1. m _ n _ _ l   _____
2. v _ l _ _ ble   _____
3. ind _ v _ d _ _ l   _____
4. amb _ t _ _ _ s   _____
5. s _ r _ _ _ s   _____
6. c _ _ t _ _ n   _____
7. c _ _ p _ r _ t _   _____
8. v _ c _ _ m   _____
9. r _ _ l _ z _   _____
10. pr _ cl _ _ m   _____
11. r _ l _ _ ble   _____
12. l _ _ _ t _ nant   _____
13. _ ppr _ _ ch   _____
14. c _ _ nterf _ _ t   _____
15. n _ rv _ _ s   _____

Study List:

ambitious
approach
caution
cooperate
counterfeit
individual
lieutenant
manual
nervous
proclaim
realize
reliable
serious
vacuum
valuable

● SKILL DRILL 4

Answer the following questions by using words from the Study List.

Which words contain the vowel combination *ua*?

1. _____   2. _____

3. _____

Which word contains the vowel combination *ai*?

4. _____

Which word contains the vowel combination *ia*?

5. _____

Which word contains the vowel combination *ieu*?

6. _____

Which word contains the vowel combination *oa*?

7. _____

Which words contain the vowel combination *ou*?

8. _____   9. _____

10. _____   11. _____

Which word contains the vowel combination *au*?

12. _____

Which word contains the vowel combination *oo*?

13. _____

Which word contains the vowel combination *uu*?

14. _____

Which word contains the vowel combination *ea*?

15. _____

● WORD GAME 11

All of the letters from the words in the Study List appear in this puzzle. Cross out the letters of the puzzle as you use them to spell the Study List words. There will be enough letters left over to answer the question below.

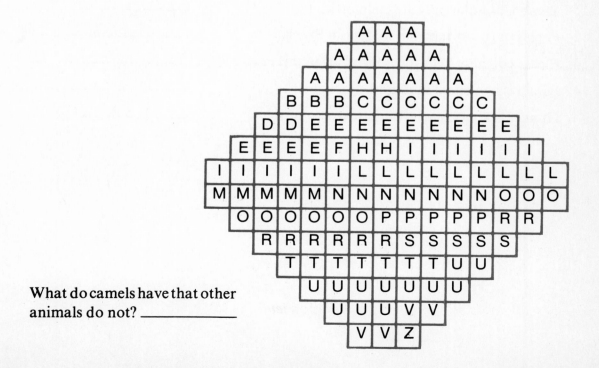

What do camels have that other animals do not? _____

● HOW WELL CAN YOU SPELL?

Try to take this practice test without looking back at Lesson 11. After you have finished, check your work against the Study List. Correct any mistakes you have made.

A. One word in each of the following pairs of words is spelled incorrectly. Circle that word and spell it correctly on the line provided.

1. proclame, cooperate   _____

2. serious, realice   _____

3. individual, vacume   _____

4. aproach, valuable   _____

5. nervous, manuale   _____

6. ambitous, counterfeit   _____

7. lutenant, reliable   _____

8. caushun, proclaim   _____

B. In each of the following sentences, one word is spelled incorrectly. Find that word. Then spell it correctly on the line provided.

9. The accident taught Joanne a valueable lesson.   _____

10. The performers were nerveous before the curtain
     went up.   _____

11. Those ten-dollar bills are counterfit.   _____

12. Pete is the most relyable student in the class.   _____

13. Please coperate with the police during this emergency. _____

14. Dinah is a talented individule.   _____

15. Hunger is a serius problem in most countries.   _____

12 Free Wheeling

They use no gas. They don't pollute. They're great for exercise, as well as transportation. And with a little practice, anyone can ride one. In case you haven't already guessed, this machine runs on human power—the bicycle!

Bikes haven't always been easy to use. The first one was invented in 1690, and looked more like a scooter. It had two wheels and a board that was pushed around with the feet. This bike traveled in a straight line because there was no way to steer it. Doctors were quick to criticize the invention. They warned that it was harmful to people's health. It seems that all the pushing was hurting people's legs.

To solve the medical problem, someone invented pedals. Actually, these pedals were cranks. But they weren't pushed by the feet. Riders had to lie on the frame of the bike and turn the cranks with their hands! No one is sure exactly what this did to people's hands. Nevertheless, the bicycle industry continued to grow.

In those days, bicycles came in all sorts of shapes and sizes. Some had large rear wheels and small front ones, while others had just the opposite. But the great-granddaddy of the bicycle, as we know it today, was built in 1885. This cycle had two equal-sized wheels and it had a chain. It was called "The Rover," and was very popular.

Cycling was a big hit in the late 1800s. People did all sorts of crazy things on bikes. A man named Tom Stevens rode his bike around the world. It took him two years to complete the trip. That was pretty good time, considering that in many countries there were no roads.

With the invention of the automobile, the bicycle's popularity died down. Today bikes are coasting to a comeback. Let's hear it for pedal power!

● REVIEWING YOUR READING

Circle the letter beside the word or phrase that best completes the sentence.

1. Bicycles
   a. pollute the air.
   b. use gasoline.
   c. provide no exercise.
   d. are a source of transportation.

2. The first bicycle looked like
   a. a roller skate.
   b. a scooter.
   c. a wagon.
   d. an automobile.

3. The first bicycle was known to hurt people's
   a. fingers.
   b. heads.
   c. legs.
   d. arms.

4. Some early bicycles had
   a. two front wheels.
   b. three rear wheels.
   c. large rear wheels.
   d. four small rear wheels.

5. The first bike, as we know it today, was called the
   a. tricycle.
   b. unicycle.
   c. "Rover."
   d. clover.

6. Cycling was very popular in the late
   a. 1300s.
   b. 1500s.
   c. 1600s.
   d. 1800s.

7. A man named Tom Stevens
   a. rode his bike around the world.
   b. invented a motor-driven bike.
   c. invented a chain-driven bike.
   d. rode his bike to the North Pole.

8. According to the story, you can conclude that
   a. bicycles replaced autos as transportation.
   b. bicycles are harmful to your health.
   c. automobiles replaced bicycles as transportation.
   d. automobiles are driven by chains.

● FIGURING THE FACTS

Decide whether the following statements are true or false. Write **T** on the line if the statement is true. If the statement is false, change the statement to make it true. Cross out the incorrect word or phrase in the sentence. Then, if necessary, write the correct word or phrase on the line.

1. With a little practice, almost anyone can ride a bike. _____

2. Bicycles run on electric power. _____

3. The first bike was invented in 1960. _____

4. The first bike was pushed by the feet. _____

5. The first bike only traveled in a straight line. _____

6. On one type of bike, the rider had to lie down. _____

7. Some bikes had large rear wheels. _____

8. "The Rover" was invented in 1885. _____

9. "The Rover" was a motor-driven bicycle. _____

10. It took Tom Stevens ten years to ride around the world. _____

● WHAT'S YOUR OPINION?

1. Why do you think the automobile took the place of the bicycle as a means of transportation?

_____

_____

_____

_____

2. Do you think that bicycles are the answer to today's transportation problems? Why or why not?

_____

_____

_____

_____

● DEVELOPING SPELLING SKILLS

Study List

The following words appear in the reading selection.

exercise   **practice**   **criticize**

Because the endings of these words look and sound somewhat alike, the endings are often confused. When learning the words in this chapter, it is most important to pay close attention to the endings in each.

accomplice
advertise
apprentice
criticize
disguise
exercise
improvise
itemize
patronize
practice
prejudice
revise
splice
standardize
summarize

On your left is a Study List of words. Each ends in either *ise*, *ice*, or *ize*. Be careful of the endings when you memorize these words!

● SKILL DRILL 1

Rewrite each of the following words on the lines provided. Then circle the *ise, ize,* or *ice* ending in each.

1. prejudice _____
2. patronize _____
3. standardize _____
4. disguise _____
5. improvise _____
6. apprentice _____
7. summarize _____

8. practice _____
9. itemize _____
10. accomplice _____
11. criticize _____
12. exercise _____
13. advertise _____
14. splice _____

15. revise _____

● SKILL DRILL 2

The following are short definitions of words from the Study List. Fill the blanks with words from the Study List that match the definitions. If you need help, check the Mini-Dictionary in the back of this book.

1. To make something up as you go along _____
2. Activity that improves the body _____
3. A person learning a trade or art _____
4. To give public notice in a newspaper or on TV, etc. _____
5. To make a summary of _____
6. To join together _____
7. To make corrections or improvements _____
8. An opinion formed without judging fairly _____
9. Action done over and over for skill _____
10. To be a regular customer of something _____
11. To list by items _____
12. To make standard in size, weight, shape, etc. _____
13. A person who aids another in committing a crime _____
14. A change in appearance to look like someone else _____
15. To find fault with something _____

● SKILL DRILL 3

Complete each of the following words by adding either *ise, ize,* or *ice* to form words from the Study List. Write the words you have formed on the lines provided.

1. item _ _ _   _____
2. accompl _ _ _   _____
3. improv _ _ _   _____
4. apprent _ _ _   _____
5. patron _ _ _   _____
6. critic _ _ _   _____
7. summar _ _ _   _____

8. standard _ _ _   _____
9. prejud _ _ _   _____
10. exerc _ _ _   _____
11. advert _ _ _   _____
12. disgu _ _ _   _____
13. pract _ _ _   _____
14. spl _ _ _   _____

15. rev _ _ _   _____

● SKILL DRILL 4

Answer the following questions by using words from the Study List.

Which words end in *ice*?

1. _____   2. _____
3. _____   4. _____
5. _____

Which words end in *ise*?

6. _____   7. _____
8. _____   9. _____
10. _____

Which words end in *ize*?

11. _____   12. _____
13. _____   14. _____
15. _____

Study List

accomplice
advertise
apprentice
criticize
disguise
exercise
improvise
itemize
patronize
practice
prejudice
revise
splice
standardize
summarize

● WORD GAME 12

The words from the Study List are hidden in this puzzle. They read from top to bottom, left to right, and diagonally. Circle the words you find. Make sure they are spelled correctly. When you find a word, cross it off the list.

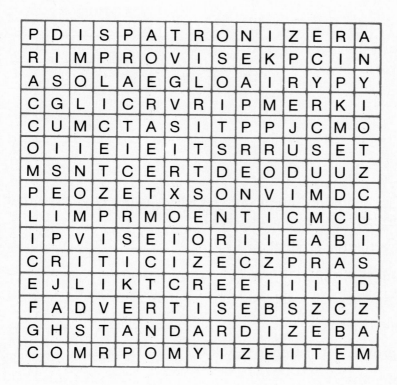

Study List

accomplice
advertise
apprentice
criticize
disguise
exercise
improvise
itemize
patronize
practice
prejudice
revise
splice
standardize
summarize

● HOW WELL CAN YOU SPELL?

Try to take this practice test without looking back at Lesson 12. After you have finished, check your work against the Study List. Correct any mistakes you have made.

A. One word in each of the following pairs of words is spelled incorrectly. Circle that word and spell it correctly on the line provided.

1. disguize, improvise   _____

2. accomplise, patronize   _____

3. itemize, splise   _____

4. prejudice, summarice   _____

5. criticice, standardize   _____

6. exercize, advertise   _____

7. revize, practice   _____

8. apprentise, splice   _____

B. In each of the following sentences, one word is spelled incorrectly. Find that word. Then spell it correctly on the line provided.

9. Our company will advertize the product on TV.   _____

10. Riding a bicycle takes plenty of practize.   _____

11. Please itemise all the supplies you will need.   _____

12. Ted was first to patronice our shop.   _____

13. Joanna will try to improvize her speech to the class.   _____

14. Try to vote without prejudise.   _____

15. Exact measurements will help to standardice our
    baked goods.   _____

13 Her Best Shot

When Maren Seidler was 13, her father told her, "See this iron ball? I think that with this you'll see all the countries of the world." With her father as her first coach, Maren managed to break the shot-put record for her age group. She has traveled the globe competing. Today she is the best female shot-putter in American history.

"Even if it's done well, not many spectators get much out of seeing it," says Maren. She refers to the fact that shot-putting does not attract many people—either as players or as watchers. Few people have knowledge of the sport. Even fewer realize that it is a sport for women as well as men.

Shot-putting is a simple contest of strength and balance. A shot-putter must throw an iron ball from inside a seven-foot (two-meter) circle. Like a dancer, the shot-putter must have complete body control. The athlete must put all her or his energy into throwing the iron ball, without leaving the circle. The iron ball is called a shot. A women's shot weighs 8 pounds 13 ounces (4 kilograms). The men's is about twice as heavy. Maren holds the American Women's record for hurling this cannonball. She has thrown it a distance of 62 feet 7¾ inches (18 meters). That's almost a quarter the length of a football field!

Music is Maren's inspiration. "I crave music," she says. She listens to classical music in the morning "to awaken with clarity." Before training, she listens to rock music "to really blast." And at night it's rhythm and blues. All that music must be doing the trick. Maren has won over 20 national shot-putting titles.

● REVIEWING YOUR READING

Circle the letter beside the word or phrase that best completes the sentence.

1. Maren Seidler is the best female

   a. runner in the world.
   b. shot-putter in American history.
   c. runner in American history.
   d. shot-putter in the world.

2. Shot-putting is a sport for

   a. dancers.
   b. runners.
   c. women only.
   d. both men and women.

3. Shot-putters throw

   a. a bowling ball.
   b. a copper ball.
   c. an iron ball.
   d. a rubber ball.

4. Shot-putters must throw the ball from within a

   a. 3-foot (0.9-meter) circle.
   b. 5-foot (1.5-meter) square.
   c. 7-foot (2-meter) circle.
   d. 9-foot (2.7-meter) square.

5. The ball shot-putters use is called a

   a. shot.
   b. put.
   c. weight.
   d. bomb.

6. Maren Seidler's inspiration is

   a. television.
   b. books.
   c. music.
   d. movies.

7. Maren Seidler holds the women's

   a. American shot-put record.
   b. European shot-put record.
   c. American running record.
   d. Russian gymnastics record.

8. According to the story, you can conclude that Maren became interested in shot put through her

   a. gym teacher.
   b. father.
   c. mother.
   d. English teacher.

● FIGURING THE FACTS

Decide whether the following statements are true or false. Write **T** on the line if the statement is true. If the statement is false, change the statement to make it true. Cross out the incorrect word or phrase in the sentence. Then, if necessary, write the correct word or phrase on the line.

1. Maren has competed all over the globe. _____

2. Maren's first coach was her brother. _____

3. At the age of 13, Maren broke the world shot-put record. _____

4. Shot-putting does not attract many people. _____

5. Shot-putting is a simple test of quickness. _____

6. The shot-putter must have complete body control. _____

7. The women's shot weighs more than the men's. _____

8. Maren has thrown the shot more than half the length of a football field. _____

9. Maren listens to classical music just before training. _____

10. Maren has won 150 national titles. _____

● WHAT'S YOUR OPINION?

1. The women's shot weighs less than the men's. Do you think they should be equal? Why or why not?

_____

_____

_____

_____

2. Why do you think that shot-putting is not a popular sport?

_____

_____

_____

_____

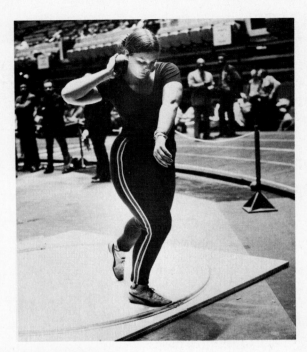

● DEVELOPING SPELLING SKILLS

**Study
List**

The following words appear in the reading selection.

managed   knowledge   spectators   attract

Words like these pose special problems in spelling. For example, *managed* and *knowledge* have the same *j* sound but it is spelled differently in each. This *j* sound can be spelled *g, ge, dge,* and, of course, *j*. The most confusing are the words in which the sound is spelled *g* or *dge,* as in *managed* and *knowledge.*

Words like *spectators* and *attract* contain the letter combination *ct.* In spelling words with this consonant combination, it's easy to forget either the *c* or the *t.*

On your left is a Study List of words. Some are examples of the *j* sound spelled *ge* or *dge,* while others contain the *ct* consonant combination.

attract
compact
construct
distract
impact
inspector
knowledge
language
managed
mileage
privilege
salvage
spectators
vegetable
wreckage

● SKILL DRILL 1

Rewrite each of the following words on the lines provided. Then circle the *ge, dge,* or *ct* in each.

1. vegetable   _____

2. privilege   _____

3. inspector   _____

4. mileage   _____

5. language   _____

6. wreckage   _____

7. construct   _____

8. salvage   _____

9. spectators   _____

10. impact   _____

11. managed   _____

12. knowledge   _____

13. distract   _____

14. compact   _____

15. attract   _____

● SKILL DRILL 2

The following are short definitions of words from the Study List. Fill the blanks with words from the Study List that match the definitions. If you need help, check the Mini-Dictionary in the back of this book.

1. Human speech, spoken or written   _____

2. Controlled or handled   _____

3. Miles covered or traveled   _____

4. The remains of something ruined   _____

5. A special right or advantage   _____

6. A person who checks or looks over carefully   _____

7. People who watch an event   _____

8. To rescue or save from being thrown away   _____

9. A plant used for food   _____

10. To draw something or someone to oneself   _____

11. What one knows   _____

12. Firmly packed together; small   _____

13. To put together or build   _____

14. Draw away, confuse, or disturb   _____

15. Collision; the striking of one thing against another   _____

● SKILL DRILL 3

Fill in the blanks in each of the following words to form words from the Study List. Then write the words you have formed on the lines provided.

1. con _ _ ru _ _ _____
2. sp _ _ _ at _ _ s _____
3. v _ _ _ table _____
4. lan _ _ a _ _ _____
5. mile _ _ _ _____
6. in _ _ e _ _ or _____
7. di _ _ ra _ _ _____

8. comp _ _ _ _____
9. salv _ _ _ _____
10. attr _ _ _ _____
11. man _ _ _ d _____
12. pri _ _ le _ _ _____
13. kn _ _ le _ _ _ _____
14. _ _ eck _ _ _ _____

15. imp _ _ _ _____

● SKILL DRILL 4

Answer the following questions by using words from the Study List.

Which words contain the word part *spect*?

1. _____   2. _____

Which word contains the word *table*?

3. _____

Which word contains the word *ledge*?

4. _____

Which word contains the word part *lege*?

5. _____

Which words contain the word *act*?

6. _____   7. _____

8. _____   9. _____

Which word contains the word part *struct*?

10. _____

Which words contain the word *age*?

11. _____   12. _____

Study List

attract
compact
construct
distract
impact
inspector
knowledge
language
managed
mileage
privilege
salvage
spectators
vegetable
wreckage

13. _____   14. _____

15. _____

● WORD GAME 13

The words from the Study List are scrambled on the left. Unscramble each word and write it correctly in the spaces on the right. If you unscramble the words correctly, you will find the answer to the puzzle question by reading the shaded column downward. Write your answer on the line below.

TRAATTC

APMOCCT

ROTATCEPSS

VSLAGEA

MIPCAT

REWKCGAE

EGAUGNAL

SNOCTURTC

SPNICEOTR

NOKLWDEGE

ANAGMED

GEEVATLBE

SIDARTCT

MEGAELI

RIPVELGEI

What did Maren Seidler's father tell her to do in order to see the world? _____

●HOW WELL CAN YOU SPELL?

Try to take this practice test without looking back at Lesson 13. After you have finished, check your work against the Study List. Correct any mistakes you have made.

A. One word in each of the following pairs of words is spelled incorrectly. Circle that word and spell it correctly on the line provided.

1. wreckadge, salvage   _____

2. language, miledge   _____

3. specktators, managed   _____

4. construct, priviledge   _____

5. distrat, compact   _____

6. inspektor, vegetable   _____

7. impakt, knowledge   _____

8. attract, salvadge   _____

B. In each of the following sentences, one word is spelled incorrectly. Find that word. Then spell it correctly on the line provided.

9. Compaked cars get much better mileage.   _____

10. Football attracks many spectators.   _____

11. It is always good to have a green vegitable with dinner. _____

12. Next year the students will be studying a foreign languadge.   _____

13. The engineers will construkt a bridge across the river. _____

14. The climbers managed to descend the mountain unharmed.   _____

15. This job requires a knowlege of science and chemistry. _____

14 André

"What a relief," said Harry Goodridge as he saw André swim into the harbor. André hopped out of the water and greeted his adopted father with a handshake and a slobbery kiss. The kiss was especially wet and slobbery since André is a seal.

More than ten years ago, Goodridge found André at the entrance to Rockport Harbor in Maine. The playful pup was jumping in and out of fishing boats. Sometimes André would tip the boats over. This would always cause confusion. At first people were amused. But soon they got tired of losing their daily catch of fish to the hungry seal. It seems that when André would tip over a boat, he would also get a delicious dinner. Goodridge decided to take André in before the seal wound up in someone's net. So he built André a 32-foot (9-meter) pen overlooking the harbor.

The winters in Rockport, Maine, are very severe. For this reason, Goodridge made plans for André to spend the winter months at the New England Aquarium in Boston. Every spring the workers at the Aquarium drain André's tank and lead him to the Atlantic Ocean. André dives in and swims a distance of 160 miles (257 kilometers) to his home in Rockport's harbor. Goodridge is always relieved when he sees André enter the harbor. He fears that someday André will meet a female seal and forget about his harbor home.

Today André is the town hero of Rockport. The people have built a statue of André. Tourists come from miles just to see his whiskered face and handsome blue-gray fur coat. They also come to catch André's daily performance. At four o'clock every day, André does a series of stunts for the crowd to earn his daily allowance of fish. Following the show, Goodridge passes a bucket through the crowd for donations. After all, fish are expensive, especially when you're feeding a 220-pound (99.8-kilogram) seal!

● REVIEWING YOUR READING

Circle the letter beside the word or phrase that best completes the sentence.

1. André is a

    a. boy.
    b. dolphin.
    c. seal.
    d. dog.

2. Harry Goodridge found André at the entrance to

    a. Boston Harbor.
    b. Rockport Harbor.
    c. Rockaway Harbor.
    d. New York Harbor.

3. When Goodridge found André he was

    a. jumping in and out of fishing boats.
    b. jumping in and out of house boats.
    c. performing tricks for tourists.
    d. working at the aquarium.

4. Goodridge built André a

    a. 23-foot (7-meter) pool.
    b. 23-foot (7-meter) pen.
    c. 32-foot (9-meter) pen.
    d. 32-foot (9-meter) boat.

5. The winters in Rockport, Maine, are

    a. very mild.
    b. very severe.
    c. sunny and warm.
    d. fair and warm.

6. André spends his winters at the

    a. Rockport Harbor.
    b. Rockport Aquarium.
    c. Miami Aquarium.
    d. New England Aquarium.

7. André's swimming trip from Boston to Maine is

    a. 64 miles (103 km.).
    b. 160 miles (257 km.).
    c. 1000 miles (1609 km.).
    d. 3000 miles (4828 km.).

8. According to the story, you can conclude that today the people of Rockport

    a. dislike André.
    b. like André.
    c. want André to leave town.
    d. wish André was a whale.

● FIGURING THE FACTS

Decide whether the following statements are true or false. Write **T** on the line if the statement is true. If the statement is false, change the statement to make it true. Cross out the incorrect word or phrase in the sentence. Then, if necessary, write the correct word or phrase on the line.

1. Harry Goodridge is André's adopted father. _____

2. André was tipping over boats in order to eat. _____

3. André's pen overlooks the town library. _____

4. André dislikes the taste of fresh fish. _____

5. Each spring the aquarium workers lead André to the Pacific Ocean. _____

6. André swims 160 miles (257 kilometers) to Rockport's harbor. _____

7. The town of Rockport put up a painting of André. _____

8. André has a handsome blue-gray fur coat. _____

9. André earns his dinner by singing. _____

10. André weighs 220 pounds (99.8 kilograms). _____

● WHAT'S YOUR OPINION?

1. Do you think that André should be allowed to roam free? Why or why not?

_____

_____

_____

_____

_____

2. What would you do if you found an animal that was hungry and in danger of being killed?

_____

_____

_____

_____

_____

● DEVELOPING SPELLING SKILLS

**Study
List**

acceptance
acquaintance
advance
allowance
appearance
assistance
clearance
distance
endurance
entrance
ignorance
importance
insurance
performance
remembrance

The following words appear in the reading selection.

allowance   distance   entrance   performance

All of these words end with the suffix *ance*. These words are often confused with words that end in *ence*. There is no rule governing these endings. Therefore, these words must be memorized.

On your left is a Study List of words. All end with the suffix *ance*. The words may look difficult because they are long. However, many are simply longer forms of words you have already studied. For example, *allowance* is *allow* plus the suffix *ance*. You will find that these words will be easy to spell once you begin to work with them. In the next chapter we will work with words that end in *ence*. If you know these words you will have little trouble learning those in the next chapter.

● SKILL DRILL 1

Rewrite each of the following words on the lines provided. Then circle the *ance* ending in each.

1. insurance _____
2. acquaintance _____
3. ignorance _____
4. performance _____
5. advance _____
6. appearance _____
7. clearance _____

8. acceptance _____
9. entrance _____
10. importance _____
11. remembrance _____
12. allowance _____
13. assistance _____
14. distance _____

15. endurance _____

● SKILL DRILL 2

The following are short definitions of words from the Study List. Fill the blanks with words from the Study List that match the definitions. If you need help, check the Mini-Dictionary in the back of this book.

1. The quality of being important _____
2. Insuring of life, person, or property _____
3. The acting of a show, movie, etc. _____
4. The act of remembering _____
5. To move forward _____
6. Help or aid _____
7. The act of clearing a space _____
8. Power to keep on or last _____
9. The act of taking something offered or given _____
10. The space between two things, places, or people _____
11. A person you know but not as a close friend _____
12. The place through which to enter _____
13. A lack of knowledge _____
14. A limited share of money or goods that is allowed to be given _____
15. The act of coming into sight or appearing _____

● SKILL DRILL 3

Fill the blanks in each of the following words to form a word from the Study List. Then write the word you have formed on the line provided.

1. a _ _ ear _ nce   _____   8. im _ _ _ t _ nce   _____

2. en _ r _ nce   _____   9. in _ _ _ _ nce   _____

3. en _ ur _ nce   _____   10. per _ _ _ mance   _____

4. a _ _ i _ t _ nce   _____   11. a _ _ ow _ nce   _____

5. a _ _ _ a _ nt _ nce_____   12. a _ _ e _ _ _ nce   _____

6. dis _ _ nce   _____   13. ad _ _ nce   _____

7. r _ _ _ _ br _ nce   _____   14. cl _ _ r _ nce   _____

15. ig _ _ r _ nce   _____

● SKILL DRILL 4

Answer the following questions by using words from the Study List.

Which words begin with the prefix *en* ?

1. _____   2. _____

Which word begins with the prefix *in* ?

3. _____

Which word begins with the prefix *dis* ?

4. _____

Which word begins with the prefix *re* ?

5. _____

Which word begins with the prefix *ad* ?

6. _____

Which word contains the word part *ignor* ?

7. _____

Which word contains the word *appear*?

8. _____

Which word contains the word *assist*?

9. _____

Which word contains the word *import*?

10. _____

Which word contains the word *perform*?

11. _____

Which word contains the word *acquaint*?

12. _____

Which word contains the word *allow*?

13. _____

Which word contains the word *accept*?

14. _____

Which word contains the word *clear*?

15. _____

Study List

acceptance
acquaintance
advance
allowance
appearance
assistance
clearance
distance
endurance
entrance
ignorance
importance
insurance
performance
remembrance

● **WORD GAME 14**

This is a puzzle without any clues! Study the length and spelling of each Study List word. Then figure out which words from the Study List fit into the spaces. Once you have found the first word, the others will be easy to find. Some of the letters have been given to you.

● HOW WELL CAN YOU SPELL?

Try to take this practice test without looking back at Lesson 14. After you have finished, check your work against the Study List. Correct any mistakes you have made.

A. One word in each of the following pairs of words is spelled incorrectly. Circle that word and spell it correctly on the line provided.

1. ignorence, insurance _____

2. acceptance, remembrence _____

3. clearence, entrance _____

4. allowence, endurance _____

5. distance, acquaintence _____

6. performance, advance _____

7. importance, assistence _____

8. appearence, ignorance _____

B. In each of the following sentences, one word is spelled incorrectly. Find that word. Then spell it correctly on the line provided.

9. The distence between the two cities is 50 miles (80 km.). _____

10. Joanne received her letter of acceptence today. _____

11. You should have an insurence policy for your car. _____

12. Please wait for me by the entrence. _____

13. James will advence in his company. _____

14. Hiking is a test of strength and endurence. _____

15. Ed isn't aware of the importence of knowing mathematics. _____

15 Boston's Power Hitter

The place was Detroit's Tiger Stadium. The year was 1975. An audience of baseball fans looked on as the pitcher hurled a low ball just outside of home plate. The man at bat made a sturdy swing and struck the ball. A sharp cracking sound rang through the stadium. The ball didn't go very far, but the bat did. It broke in two! One half flew over to the Tigers' dugout. The other was left in the batter's hands. He stood there staring in disbelief. The powerful presence holding a piece of the baseball bat was Jim Rice—batting star of the Boston Red Sox.

Jim Rice has been called the most powerful hitter in the American League. His record of home runs gets higher each year. In 1978, he was the first American Leaguer to get over 400 total bases (406) since Joe DiMaggio in 1937. It is little wonder that at the end of the 1978 season he was voted Most Valuable Player.

"My strength comes from my wrists and legs," says Rice. He uses his body weight to "jump out" at the ball. He has the confidence to know that his hitting doesn't need improvement. As Jim says, "My hitting is a natural thing." However, he's had to work hard to learn to play the outfield. He has dedicated himself to improving his fielding skills. Already he has proved himself better than average.

Jim was born and educated in South Carolina. He had eight brothers and sisters. His father worked in a factory. High school athletics had a big influence on Jim's career. He was his school's all-round star in baseball, football, and basketball. "I wanted to play pro-basketball," Jim says, "but I wasn't tall enough." Jim was eighteen when the Boston Red Sox made him an offer. The team's scout came to Jim's house with $45,000 and a contract. "That decided it for baseball," Rice says. Today he's one of the highest paid players in the American League.

Jim lives with his wife and young son just outside of Boston, Mass. He likes his privacy. His friends say that his frown has scared quite a few reporters away. But they are also quick to note that his smile would "make you melt."

● **REVIEWING YOUR READING**

Circle the letter beside the word or phrase that best completes the sentence.

1. Jim Rice is the star hitter for the

    a. Detroit Red Sox.
    b. Detroit Tigers.
    c. Boston Red Sox.
    d. Chicago Cubs.

2. When Jim broke the bat in Detroit, half of it flew

    a. to the outfield.
    b. over the fence.
    c. into the stadium.
    d. to the Tigers' dugout.

3. In his league, Jim has scored more runs than anyone since

    a. Babe Ruth.
    b. Reggie Jackson.
    c. Joe DiMaggio.
    d. Hank Aaron.

4. At the end of the 1978 season Jim Rice was voted

    a. Most Popular Player.
    b. Most Valuable Player.
    c. Best Hitter.
    d. Player of the Year.

5. Jim says that his hitting strength comes from his

    a. wrists and legs.
    b. shoulders and arms.
    c. back and legs.
    d. arms and feet.

6. Jim has had to work on improving his

    a. batting skills.
    b. running skills.
    c. fielding skills.
    d. pitching skills.

7. During high school Jim wanted to play professional

    a. baseball.
    b. basketball.
    c. football.
    d. soccer.

8. The Red Sox offered Jim a contract when he was

    a. eighteen.
    b. nineteen.
    d. twenty-eight.
    d. twenty-nine.

● FIGURING THE FACTS

Decide whether the following statements are true or false. Write **T** on the line if the statement is true. If the statement is false, change the statement to make it true. Cross out the incorrect word or phrase in the sentence. Then, if necessary, write the correct word or phrase on the line.

1. Jim Rice broke a baseball bat at Fenway Park. _____

2. One half of the bat stayed in Jim's hands. _____

3. Jim's record of home runs gets lower each year. _____

4. In 1978, Jim Rice was voted Most Valuable Player. _____

5. Jim uses his body weight to "jump out" at the ball. _____

6. Jim says that his hitting needs improvement. _____

7. Jim is dedicated to improving his pitching skills. _____

8. High school athletics had a big influence on Jim's career. _____

9. In high school Jim played baseball, football, and soccer. _____

10. Today Jim is one of the highest paid players in the National League. _____

● WHAT'S YOUR OPINION?

1. Jim Rice's confidence in his talent has brought him a long way. Why do you think it is important to have confidence in yourself?

_____

_____

_____

_____

2. Jim had talent in hitting, but he had to work hard at his fielding. Do you think having talent is enough to make you a success?

_____

_____

_____

_____

● DEVELOPING SPELLING SKILLS

Study List

The following words appear in the reading selection.

audience   presence   confidence   influence

All of these words end with the suffix *ence*. Words that end with this suffix are often confused with words that end in *ance*. As you saw in Lesson 14, there is no rule to tell us when to use *ence* and when to use *ance*. Therefore, these words must be memorized.

On your left is a Study List of words. All the words end in *ence*. Be sure to learn these words well. These words may look difficult because they are long, but actually most of them are quite easy to spell.

absence
audience
circumference
coincidence
commence
confidence
convenience
correspondence
difference
existence
experience
independence
influence
presence
reference

● SKILL DRILL 1

Rewrite each of the following words on the lines provided. Then circle the *ence* ending in each.

1. correspondence _____

2. experience _____

3. commence _____

4. presence _____

5. reference _____

6. absence _____

7. existence _____

8. difference _____

9. influence _____

10. confidence _____

11. convenience _____

12. independence _____

13. audience _____

14. circumference _____

15. coincidence _____

● SKILL DRILL 2

The following are short definitions of words from the Study List. Fill the blanks with words from the Study List that match the definitions. If you need help, check the Mini-Dictionary in the back of this book.

1. Freedom from control or help of another _____

2. Quality of being convenient or handy _____

3. A chance meeting that is remarkable _____

4. A firm belief in oneself _____

5. Everything you have ever felt or done, or what has happened to you _____

6. The condition of being different; unlikeness _____

7. An exchange of letters, or letter writing _____

8. To start or begin _____

9. People gathered in a place to hear or see something _____

10. The boundary line of a circle _____

11. Life; the state of being _____

12. To have power over another _____

13. The state of being away _____

14. The state of being present _____

15. The act of referring or consulting _____

● SKILL DRILL 3

Fill the blanks in each of the following words to form words from the Study List. Then write the word you have formed on the line provided.

1. p _ _ s _ nce   _____

2. a _ _ _ nce   _____

3. in _ _ u _ nce   _____

4. cir _ _ m _ _ r _ nce _____

5. co _ _ en _ _   _____

6. co _ fi _ _ nce   _____

7. di _ _ er _ nce   _____

8. con _ _ n _ _ nce   _____

9. in _ _ pen _ _ nce   _____

10. c _ _ nci _ _ nce   _____

11. e _ _ er _ _ nce   _____

12. c _ rr _ _ pon _ _ nce _____

13. a _ d _ _ nce   _____

14. e _ is _ _ nce   _____

15. r _ _ e _ _ nce   _____

● SKILL DRILL 4

Answer the following questions by using words from the Study List.

Which words begin with the prefix *con*?

1. _____   2. _____

Which words begin with the prefix *in*?

3. _____   4. _____

Which word begins with the prefix *circum*?

5. _____

Which word begins with the prefix *ab*?

6. _____

Which word contains the word *refer*?

7. _____

Which word contains the word *differ*?

8. _____

Which word contains the word *correspond*?

9. _____

Study List

absence
audience
circumference
coincidence
commence
confidence
convenience
correspondence
difference
existence
experience
independence
influence
presence
reference

Which word contains the word *coincide*?

10. _____

Which word begins with the prefix *pre*?

11. _____

Which words begin with the prefix *ex*?

12. _____   13. _____

Which word begins with the prefix *com*?

14. _____

Which word begins with the prefix *audi*?

15. _____

● WORD GAME 15

This is a puzzle without any clues! Study the length and spelling of each Study List word. Then figure out which words from the Study List fit in the spaces. Once you have found the first word, the rest will be easy to find. Some of the letters have been given to you.

● HOW WELL CAN YOU SPELL?

Try to take this practice test without looking back at Lesson 15. After you have finished, check your work against the Study List. Correct any mistakes you have made.

A. One word in each of the following pairs of words is spelled incorrectly. Circle that word and spell it correctly on the line provided.

1. existance, difference   _____

2. conveniance, influence   _____

3. independence, presance   _____

4. referance, experience   _____

5. coincidance, confidence   _____

6. circumferance, absence   _____

7. correspondance, reference   _____

8. commance, audience   _____

B. In each of the following sentences, one word is spelled incorrectly. Find that word. Then spell it correctly on the line provided.

9. Don is working at the restaurant to get experiance
   cooking.   _____

10. You will have to make up that absance from class.   _____

11. The audiance stood as the president entered the room.   _____

12. Mary has all the self-confidance she needs.   _____

13. In 1776, America declared its independance from Britain. _____

14. Television has a great influance on our culture.   _____

15. The differance between the two countries is very small. _____

16 Tuned In

Although you may not have heard of him, Nam June Paik can be called the father of music video. He was the first artist to make use of television. One of his works, called *TV Moon,* has a dozen TVs showing the rise and fall of the moon. By tinkering with electronics, Paik changes the images on TV screens. The screen is his canvas. But you'll find no country scene or bowl of fruit in this painting. Nam June certainly has a taste for the unusual.

Nam June was born in Korea, but moved to Japan when he was very young. As a child, he was fascinated by the radio. He would listen for hours and hours. Often he would ask, "Why do people hide in the box?"

With the invention of television, his interest widened. Nam June was spellbound by the magic images that appeared on the screen. Determined to study electronics, he made his way to Germany. By that time, he had already studied art and music. On the piano, he could perform everything from popular to classical music. In Germany, Nam June put his knowledge of music and electronics together. The result was electronic music. His compositions became so popular that even the Beatles became fans.

But Nam June didn't stop with success. A person who studied radar told him that radar waves made interesting patterns. "Then I had an idea," Nam June says. "Why don't I move from electronic music to electronic painting with the TV?" And he did.

In the early 1960s he had his first show of "electronic paintings." It was the world's first video art show. There were 13 TV sets with scrambled images. Paik had learned enough about televisions to be able to control the pictures the way he wanted.

Now, after 20 years of tinkering with TV sets, he is a great success. His TV art has been seen in museums around the world. He has even had a show at the famous Whitney Museum of American Art in New York. You could say that people are finally getting "turned on" by his art!

● REVIEWING YOUR READING

Circle the letter beside the word or phrase that best completes the sentence.

1. Nam June Paik can be called the

   a. father of rock music.
   b. artist of the century.
   c. father of music video.
   d. father of television.

2. Paik was the first artist to make use of

   a. radio.
   b. electricity.
   c. laser beams.
   d. television.

3. Nam June Paik was born in

   a. Korea.
   b. the United States.
   c. Japan.
   d. Germany.

4. As a child Nam June was fascinated by

   a. movies.
   b. computers.
   c. rock music.
   d. radio.

5. As a boy Nam June studied how to play the

   a. cello.
   b. piano.
   c. electric guitar.
   d. violin.

6. One of Paik's works is called

   a. *13 Moons.*
   b. *TV Moon.*
   c. *The Rise of the Moon.*
   d. *Radio Wave Moon.*

7. Nam June invented electronic painting by studying

   a. television repair.
   b. radios.
   c. radar waves.
   d. the music of the Beatles.

8. You can come to the conclusion that Nam June Paik

   a. likes to try new ideas.
   b. does not try new ideas.
   c. is not very successful.
   d. is no longer creating artworks.

● FIRST THINGS FIRST

Some of the events in Nam June Paik's life are listed below. Reread the story, paying close attention to the order in which things happened. Then write the numbers from 1 to 8 beside the sentences in the order in which things happened.

———————— He moved to Japan at a young age.

———————— The invention of TV caused him to widen his interests.

———————— Nam June composed electronic music.

———————— Paik learned about radar waves.

———————— As a boy in Japan he found the radio fascinating.

———————— He moved to Germany to study electronics.

———————— He began to use televisions to make "electronic paintings."

———————— Nam June Paik was born in Korea.

● WHAT'S YOUR OPINION?

1. Nam June Paik's art was different from anyone else's. It was original—no one had ever done anything like it. Why is it important to be original?

   _____

   _____

   _____

   _____

   _____

2. Nam June could have stopped being an artist with his first success in electronic music but he didn't. Why do you think he kept creating new things? Is it important to keep working? Why?

   _____

   _____

   _____

   _____

   _____

● DEVELOPING SPELLING SKILLS

The following words appear in the reading selection.

scene—seen

These words sound alike, but they are spelled differently. They also mean different thing

Scene means a time or place
Seen means having looked at

These words are **homophones**. A **homophone** is a word that has the same sound as another word, but a different spelling and meaning.

Below is a Study List of words. Each word is a homophone. Homophones are very easily confused. It is important to remember the spelling as well as the meaning of each. Some of these you may already know.

Study List	Definitions of Study List Words:
	ceiling—the inside top covering of a room
	sealing—closing tightly
ceiling	
sealing	council—a group of people called together to talk things over
council	counsel—to advise
counsel	
flair	flair—a natural talent
flare	flare—a dazzling burst of flame or light
morning	
mourning	morning—the early part of the day
rap	mourning—showing sorrow for someone's death
wrap	
ring	rap—to strike sharply
wring	wrap—to cover with paper and string
scene	
seen	ring—to make a clear sound by touching or striking
weather	wring—to squeeze or twist
whether	
	scene—the time or place of a play or story
	seen—having looked at
	weather—climate conditions
	whether—if

● SKILL DRILL 1

Rewrite each of the following words on the lines provided.

1. morning _____   9. scene _____
2. ceiling _____   10. sealing _____
3. council _____   11. flair _____
4. mourning _____   12. seen _____
5. whether _____   13. flare _____
6. counsel _____   14. weather _____
7. ring _____   15. wrap _____
8. rap _____   16. wring _____

● SKILL DRILL 2

The following are short definitions of words from the Study List. Fill the blanks with words from the Study List that match the definitions. If you need help, check the Mini-Dictionary in the back of this book.

1. The time or place of a play or story _____
2. A natural talent _____
3. A group of people called together to talk things over _____
4. Closing tightly _____
5. A dazzling burst of flame or light _____
6. If _____
7. Having looked at _____
8. Showing sorrow for someone's death _____
9. The inside top covering of a room _____
10. To squeeze or twist _____
11. To cover with paper and string _____
12. To strike sharply _____
13. To make a clear sound by touching or striking _____
14. Climate conditions _____
15. To advise _____
16. The early part of the day _____

• SKILL DRILL 3

Answer the following questions by using words from the Study List.

Which words end with the letters *er*?

1. _____   2. _____

Which word contains the word *air*?

3. _____

Which word contains the word *are*?

4. _____

Which words end with the letter *p*?

5. _____   6. _____

Which word contains the vowel combination *ee*?

7. _____

Which word ends with the letters *ne*?

8. _____

Which words begin with the letters *coun*?

9. _____   10. _____

Which word ends with the letters *ing*?

11. _____   12. _____

13. _____   14. _____

15. _____   16. _____

Study List

ceiling
sealing
council
counsel
flair
flare
morning
mourning
rap
wrap
ring
wring
scene
seen
weather
whether

• SKILL DRILL 4

Fill the blanks in the following sentences by choosing the correct homophone in parentheses. Write it on the line provided.

1. Our family is (morning, mourning) _____ the death of Uncle Ralph.

2. Mr. Sweeney will (council, counsel) _____ the class on career choices.

3. Mrs. Adams will be (sealing, ceiling) _____ the jars with wax.

4. The light is hanging from the (sealing, ceiling) _____ .

5. The (seen, scene) _____ of the novel is New York City.

6. Kurt has a (flare, flair) _____ for performing.

7. He asked (weather, whether) _____ he should go or not.

8. The light from the (flare, flair) _____ brightened the sky.

9. I have (seen, scene) _____ many hats like that one.

10. The (whether, weather) _____ in Chicago is rainy today.

11. (Ring, Wring) _____ the bell again to see if they are home.

12. There will be a meeting of the student (council, counsel) _____ .

13. The postmaster asks that we (rap, wrap) _____ our packages carefully.

14. Did someone (wrap, rap) _____ on the window a few minutes ago?

15. If you (wring, ring) _____ the shirt out, it will dry quickly.

16. We have a good breakfast every (morning, mourning) _____ .

● WORD GAME 16

The words from the Study List are used in this puzzle. The numbers of the clues match the numbers of the puzzle. Read the clues below. Then write your answers in the puzzle blocks.

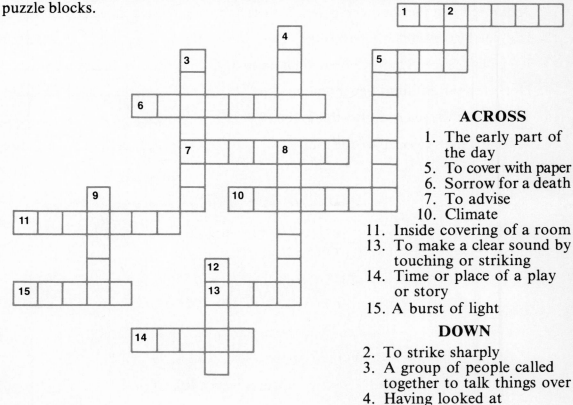

ACROSS

1. The early part of the day
5. To cover with paper
6. Sorrow for a death
7. To advise
10. Climate
11. Inside covering of a room
13. To make a clear sound by touching or striking
14. Time or place of a play or story
15. A burst of light

DOWN

2. To strike sharply
3. A group of people called together to talk things over
4. Having looked at
5. If
8. Closing tightly
9. Natural talent
12. To squeeze or twist

● HOW WELL CAN YOU SPELL?

Try to take this practice test without looking back at Lesson 16. After you have finished, check your work against the Study List. Correct any mistakes you have made.

One word in each of the following sentences is spelled incorrectly. Find that word. Then spell it correctly on the line provided.

1. If the whether permits, we'll have the picnic on Sunday. _____

2. Susan has shown a flare for drawing. _____

3. The sealing in the kitchen is quite high. _____

4. The city counsel is meeting this afternoon. _____

5. The coach will be the one to council you on athletics. _____

6. Many students have already scene the exhibit. _____

7. Ellen is morning the death of her pet cat. _____

8. The secretaries will be ceiling the envelopes with tape. _____

9. The bus will leave early tomorrow mourning. _____

10. I don't know weather or not I should go. _____

11. A flair marked the spot where the accident happened. _____

12. Did you hear the telephone wring? _____

13. Ring out the towel before you hang it up to dry. _____

14. Don't rap the gift until I get home. _____

15. The seen of the play was Boston in the 1930s. _____

16. The baby likes to wrap on the table. _____

17 Magnificent Marathon

Friends, reporters, and television crews gathered to wish Patty Wilson good luck. Her goal was to run from Buena Park, California, to Portland, Oregon. The distance is 1,000 miles (1,609 kilometers). As the music rose from the local band, Patty broke the paper banner that marked her start.

This was a most historic marathon because Patty has epilepsy. That means she suffers from a disorder that brings about seizures. Seizures are spells that cause people to shake and to black out.

On her run, Patty carried the Candle of Understanding. It is the symbol of the Epilepsy Foundation of America. She hoped to show the world that the word "handicapped" doesn't mean "unable."

During the first 25 miles (40 kilometers), Patty fractured a bone in her foot. A doctor advised her not to continue. But Patty was determined. She kept running, averaging 31 miles (49 kilometers) a day. Patty's father kept her company on the trip. At night they slept in a small van, and each morning they rose at 4:30 to prepare for running. By 6:00 A.M. they were on the road. Patty fought steep hills and stiff winds. She ignored the painful blisters on her feet. Along the way, people came out to greet her. Many were handicapped. They cheered her on and, sometimes, even ran along with her.

After six weeks, the ordeal was over. She had finally reached Portland. Crowds of well-wishers lined the streets. People cheered and waved. Some even cried. Patty could hardly smile because of the pain in her feet. But she was overjoyed. She had not only proved her point, but also set a world record for distance. The governor of Oregon proclaimed July 28 as Patty Wilson Day. It was a special day for anyone who has ever been called "handicapped." "I haven't stopped running because of my epilepsy," says Patty. "I never will."

● REVIEWING YOUR READING

Circle the letter beside the word or phrase that best completes the sentence.

1. Patty Wilson ran a total of

   a. 10 miles (16 kilometers).
   b. 100 miles (160 kilometers).
   c. 500 miles (804 kilometers).
   d. 1,000 miles (1,609 kilometers).

2. Patty ran from Buena Park, California, to

   a. Portland, Oregon.
   b. San Francisco, California.
   c. Wilson, Oregon.
   d. San Diego, California.

3. Patty suffers from

   a. broken bones.
   b. seizures.
   c. headaches.
   d. sores.

4. The symbol of the Epilepsy Foundation is the

   a. Flame of Light.
   b. Candle of Understanding.
   c. Light of Hope.
   d. Torch of Happiness.

5. During Patty's first 25 miles (40 kilometers), she

   a. fractured a bone in her foot.
   b. quit running.
   c. broke her arm.
   d. suffered a seizure.

6. Patty averaged

   a. 31 miles (49 km.) per day.
   b. 60 miles (96 km.) per day.
   c. 100 miles (160 km.) per day.
   d. 1,000 miles (1,609 km.) per day.

7. Patty's marathon took a total of

   a. 2 weeks.
   b. 6 weeks.
   c. 16 weeks.
   d. 36 weeks.

8. According to the story, you can conclude that Patty Wilson will

   a. never run again.
   b. continue to run.
   c. become a professional runner.
   d. become a running coach.

● **FIGURING THE FACTS**

Decide whether the following statements are true or false. Write **T** on the line if the statement is true. If the statement is false, change the statement to make it true. Cross out the incorrect word or phrase in the sentence. Then, if necessary, write the correct word or phrase on the line.

1. Reporters came to see Patty begin her race. _____

2. At the start of the marathon, there was a band playing. _____

3. On her run, Patty carried the American flag. _____

4. When Patty fractured a bone in her foot, the doctor told her to go on. _____

5. Patty rose at 4:30 A.M. each day. _____

6. Patty began her running at 12 noon each day. _____

7. Patty made the trip all by herself. _____

8. At the end of the marathon, there were blisters on Patty's feet. _____

9. Patty Wilson set a world record for distance. _____

10. In Oregon, July 28 is Patty Wilson Day. _____

● **WHAT'S YOUR OPINION?**

1. Why do you think Patty wanted to run her marathon?

_____

_____

_____

_____

2. Patty proved that she could do an "impossible" feat. Do you believe that people can do the "impossible"? Why or why not?

_____

_____

_____

_____

● DEVELOPING SPELLING SKILLS

Capital letters tell us that something important is ahead. The first letter of every sentence *always* begins with a capital. And capitals are *always* used when spelling someone's name. However, capitalizing can become confusing when names contain more than one word. Sometimes we aren't sure whether a word is the name of something or not. Below are some rules to use as guidelines when you are in doubt about when to use capitals.

**Study
List**

Arkansas
Atlantic Ocean
California
February
Fourth of July
Governor Orebon
June
Labor Day
Mayor Chicado
New Hampshire
Niagara Falls
September
Tuesday
United Nations
Wednesday

Rule: *Always capitalize the first word in a sentence.*

Example: Crowds of well-wishers lined the streets.

Rule: *Always capitalize days of the week, months, and holidays.*

Examples: Tuesday   June 18, 1977
Fourth of July

Notice that minor words like *of* are not capitalized.

Rule: *Always capitalize the names of people, titles, schools, and organizations.*

Examples: Patty Wilson
Governor Orebon
United Nations

Rule: *Always capitalize the names of geographical terms or places like cities, states, countries, rivers, oceans, etc.*

Examples: California   Atlantic Ocean

There are more rules for capitals, which we will cover in Lesson 18.

Above is a Study List of words. All of these words apply to the rules of capitalization. If a word is supposed to be capitalized and is not, it is considered to be misspelled. Therefore, it is doubly important to know the spelling of these words, *and* to capitalize them.

● SKILL DRILL 1

Rewrite each of the following words on the lines provided. Then circle the capital letters in each.

1. Tuesday   _____

2. Wednesday   _____

3. Atlantic Ocean   _____

4. September   _____

5. New Hampshire   _____

6. Fourth of July   _____

7. June   _____

8. United Nations   _____

9. Arkansas   _____

10. California   _____

11. Mayor Chicado   _____

12. February   _____

13. Governor Orebon   _____

14. Niagara Falls   _____

15. Labor Day   _____

● SKILL DRILL 2

Answer the following questions by using words from the Study List.

Which words are the names of states?

1. _____   2. _____

3. _____

Which words are days of the week?

4. _____   5. _____

Which words are months of the year?

6. _____   7. _____

8. _____

Which is the name of an organization?

9. _____

Which are people's titles?

10. _____   11. _____

Which words are the names of holidays?

12. _____   13. _____

Which words are the names of geographical areas?

14. _____   15. _____

● SKILL DRILL 3

In the following sentences, certain Study List words should be capitalized. Find those words. Then rewrite them, correctly capitalized, on the lines provided.

1. The new class will begin next september.   _____

2. february is the second month of the year.   _____

3. The whole family will be taking the trip to niagara falls.   _____

4. New York borders on the atlantic ocean.   _____

5. The party will be held on labor day.   _____

6. Our nation's birthday is the fourth of july.   _____

7. mayor chicado will speak at today's luncheon.   _____

8. Canada is a member of the united nations.   _____

9. Patty began her marathon on june 18, 1977.   _____

10. Jean shook the hand of governor orebon.   _____

11. This week's meeting will be held on tuesday.   _____

12. On our way west, we will travel through arkansas.   _____

13. wednesday evening will be your last chance to see the film.   _____

14. new hampshire will be the first state to hold the election.   _____

15. Marge lives in Los Angeles, california.   _____

● SKILL DRILL 4

Fill in the blanks in the following words to form words from the Study List. Then write the words you have formed on the lines provided. Be sure to capitalize where necessary.

1. se _ _ _ mber   _____

2. united n _ _ ions   _____

3. j _ ne   _____

4. t _ _ sday   _____

5. _ rk _ _ s _ s   _____

6. wed _ _ _ day   _____

7. gov _ _ n _ _ orebon   _____

8. _ eb _ _ ary   _____

9. n _ _ gara falls   _____

10. at _ _ _ tic
    oc _ _ n   _____

11. l _ b _ r day   _____

12. f _ _ rth of
    july   _____

13. may _ _
    chicado   _____

14. cal _ _ _ rn _ _   _____

15. new
    hamp _ _ ire   _____

● WORD GAME 17

The words from the Study List are used in this puzzle. The numbers of the clues match the numbers in the puzzle. Read the clues below. Then write your answers in the puzzle blocks.

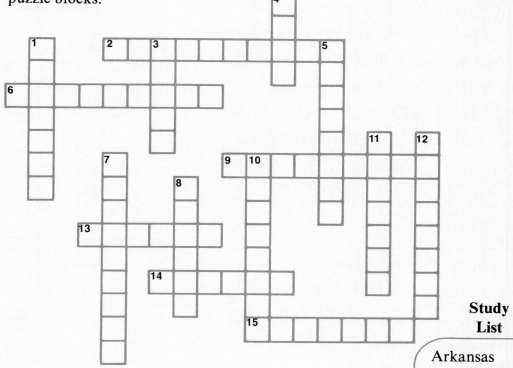

Study List

Arkansas
Atlantic Ocean
California
February
Fourth of July
Governor Orebon
June
Labor Day
Mayor Chicado
New Hampshire
Niagara Falls
September
Tuesday
United Nations
Wednesday

ACROSS
2. State that begins with capital *C*
6. ninth month
9. New _____
13. _____ Nations
14. _____ of July
15. Mayor _____

DOWN
1. Third day of the week
3. _____ Day
4. sixth month
5. State that begins with a capital *A*
7. Fourth day of the week
8. Name that begins with a capital *O*
10. _____ Ocean
11. _____ Falls
12. Second month

● HOW WELL CAN YOU SPELL?

Try to take this practice test without looking back at Lesson 17. After you have finished, check your work against the Study List. Correct any mistakes you have made.

In each of the following sentences, one word is spelled incorrectly. Find that word. Then spell it correctly on the line provided. Remember that a word is misspelled if it is not capitalized when it should be.

1. For information you must write to the new hamshire Tourist Department.   _____

2. The trip is set for the end of septimber.   _____

3. The untied nations meets in New York City.   _____

4. juen is the month that marks the beginning of summer.   _____

5. The final exam will be held on tuseday.   _____

6. arkansaw is the state next to Oklahoma.   _____

7. The parade is scheduled for wednsday morning.   _____

8. governer Orebon will be here this afternoon.   _____

9. Jody's birthday is feburary 15.   _____

10. The boat sailed close to niagra Falls.   _____

11. On this voyage, we will be crossing the Atalantic Ocean.   _____

12. This year, the vacation begins on laber Day.   _____

13. The rent is due on the forth of July.   _____

14. Carol introduced mayer Chicado to the audience.   _____

15. californa is one of the states that borders the Pacific Ocean.   _____

18 Jaws and Claws

Who could love a crocodile? They're surely not cuddly. And they aren't known for their friendly smiles. Yet the ancient Egyptians used to put gold bracelets on the legs of their toothy friends. Legend has it that they even built a city in their honor.

Today, crocodiles are more likely to end up as handbags or wallets. For this reason, "crocs" are quickly disappearing from the earth. Certain species are already extinct.

There are 21 different kinds of crocodiles. The American alligator is one of the few that is out of danger. Thanks to strict laws, the swamps of Louisiana and Florida are thick with "gators." There are so many that the government has had to hire special hunters to protect people from "troublemakers." Those are "gators" that find their way into cities and towns and threaten people's safety.

The students at the University of Florida have adopted their neighborhood gators as pets. They give names to the leathery lizards. They even pat them and feed them cookies! Experts claim that this kind of action is dangerous. The gators easily lose their natural fear of humans. Gators will attack if they feel threatened. They might even strike when looking for a tasty meal.

Although we think of crocs as violent animals, they are very good parents. When a mother croc lays her 40 to 80 eggs, the father stands guard. Mom covers the eggs with dirt and they both wait for about three months. When "peeping" sounds come from the ground, the eggs are hatching. The mother uncovers the eggs and takes the youngsters into her jaws. She carries them to their new home in a nearby pond. Both parents carefully watch the babies until they're old enough to defend themselves.

All this family talk brings us back to the question, who could love a crocodile? Why, another crocodile, of course!

● REVIEWING YOUR READING

Circle the letter beside the word or phrase that best completes the sentence.

1. Ancient Egyptians decorated crocodiles with

   a. gold hats.
   b. gold bracelets.
   c. gloves.
   d. handbags.

2. The word *extinct* means

   a. disappearing from the earth.
   b. out of style.
   c. growing.
   d. increasing in number.

3. Certain species of crocodiles are disappearing from the earth because they are being used for

   a. hats and gloves.
   b. food and clothing.
   c. handbags and wallets.
   d. jewelry and perfume.

4. The American alligator is out of danger because it is protected by

   a. hunters.
   b. students.
   c. strict laws.
   d. troublesome gators.

5. Another title for this selection could be

   a. Handbags and Wallets.
   b. Troublemakers.
   c. Florida's Pets.
   d. Gators and Crocs.

6. Feeding gators can be dangerous because they

   a. eat too much.
   b. lose their fear of humans.
   c. eat too little.
   d. lose their fear of food.

7. According to the story, you can conclude that crocodiles are

   a. good parents.
   b. poor parents.
   c. good pets.
   d. poor swimmers.

8. A mother crocodile lays

   a. 40 to 80 eggs.
   b. 80 to 100 eggs.
   c. 100 to 150 eggs.
   d. 150 to 200 eggs.

● FIGURING THE FACTS

Decide whether the following statements are true or false. Write **T** on the line if the statement is true. If the statement is false, change the statement to make it true. Cross out the incorrect word or phrase in the sentence. Then, if necessary, write the correct word or phrase on the line.

1. Legend has it that ancient Egyptians built a city in honor of the crocodile. _____

2. Crocodiles are never dangerous to humans. _____

3. There are 21 different kinds of crocodiles. _____

4. The cities in Louisiana and Florida are thick with gators. _____

5. "Troublemakers" are the gators who get into cities and towns. _____

6. Students in Florida feed cookies to gators. _____

7. Gators do not have a natural fear of humans. _____

8. If a gator feels threatened, it will attack. _____

9. Gator eggs are hatching when "peeping" sounds come from the ground. _____

10. The eggs are usually uncovered by the father. _____

● WHAT'S YOUR OPINION?

1. Do you think it is right to use animal skins for handbags, wallets, and clothing? Why or why not?

_____

_____

_____

_____

2. Do you think it is important to protect wild animals like crocodiles? Why or why not?

_____

_____

_____

_____

● DEVELOPING SPELLING SKILLS

We use capital letters to begin a sentence and when spelling the names of persons, places, or things. Here is a list of rules to use as a guideline when in doubt about using capitals. Rules 1 and 2 are new and should be studied carefully. Rules 3 through 6 are a review of rules you have learned in previous lessons.

Study List

August
Catcher in the Rye
Chinese
Egyptians
Germany
Louisiana
Mississippi River
New Year's Day
Rocky Mountains
Spanish
Sports Illustrated
Thanksgiving
The Scarlet Letter
Thursday
University of Florida

Rule 1: *Always capitalize the names of languages or adjectives that describe the people from a certain country.*

Examples: Chinese   Spanish   Egyptians

Rule 2: *Always capitalize the names of books, magazines, newspapers, and other publications.*

Examples: *The Scarlet Letter   Catcher in the Rye Sports Illustrated*

Remember that minor words like *of* or *the* are not capitalized when they are in the middle of a title.

Rule 3: *Always capitalize the first word in a sentence.*

Example: Who could love a crocodile?

Rule 4: *Always capitalize days of the week, months, and holidays.*

Examples: Thursday   August   Thanksgiving

Rule 5: *Always capitalize the names of people, titles, schools, and organizations.*

Examples: Professor John Young   University of Florida   Salvation Army

Rule 6: *Capitalize the names of geographical terms or places like cities, states, countries, rivers, mountains, etc.*

Examples: Louisiana   Germany   Potomac River
            Rocky Mountains   Atlantic Ocean

Above is a Study List of words. The rules of capitalization apply to all of these words. It is also important to know the spelling of these words. Remember, if a word is supposed to be capitalized and it is not, it is considered to be misspelled.

● **SKILL DRILL 1**

Rewrite each of the following words on the lines provided. Then circle the capital letters in each.

1. Germany _____
2. University of Florida _____
3. Thanksgiving _____
4. Thursday _____
5. *Sports Illustrated* _____
6. August _____
7. Chinese _____

8. Egyptians _____
9. New Year's Day _____
10. Spanish _____
11. Rocky Mountains _____
12. Mississippi River _____
13. *The Scarlet Letter* _____
14. *Catcher in the Rye* _____

15. Louisiana _____

● **SKILL DRILL 2**

Answer the following questions by using words from the Study List.

Which word is the name of a state?   Which word is the name of a country?

1. _____   2. _____

Which words are the names of languages?

3. _____   4. _____

Which words are geographical locations?

5. _____   6. _____

Which words are the names of holidays?

7. _____   8. _____

Which words are the names of books or magazines?

9. _____   10. _____

11. _____

Which words are the names of days or months?

12. _____   13. _____

Which is the name of a school?   Which word is the name of a nationality?

14. _____   15. _____

● SKILL DRILL 3

In the following sentences, certain Study List words should be capitalized. Find those words and rewrite them, correctly capitalized, on the lines provided.

1. Today we will talk about the people and climate of germany.   _____

2. The egyptians often decorated crocodiles with gold.   _____

3. The meeting will be held on the third day in august.   _____

4. The mississippi river flows through the state of Louisiana.   _____

5. The thursday morning class will meet on Friday.   _____

6. Please read chapter two of the *catcher in the rye*.   _____

7. Ed reads *sports illustrated* every week.   _____

8. How many people present have read *the scarlet letter*?_____

9. Patricia will be attending the university of florida next year.   _____

10. This season we will be skiing in the rocky mountains._____

11. We always have turkey on thanksgiving.   _____

12. louisiana borders on the Gulf of Mexico.   _____

13. Many of our students speak spanish.   _____

14. The parade will be held on new year's day.   _____

15. Donna knows how to say "thank you" in chinese.   _____

● SKILL DRILL 4

Fill the blanks in the following words to form words from the Study List. Then write the words you have formed on the lines provided. Be sure to capitalize where necessary.

1. *sp _ rts*
   _ ll _ str _ ted   _____

2. *ca _ _ _ er in the r _ e*   _____

3. th _ rsd _ y   _____

4. mi _ _ i _ _ i _ _ i
   river   _____

5. a _ g _ st   _____

6. e _ _ pti _ ns   _____

7. g _ rm _ ny   _____

8. ch _ n _ s _   _____

9. new _ e _ r's day   _____

10. sp _ n _ sh   _____

11. l _ _ _ s _ _ na   _____

12. th _ nk _ g _ v _ ng   _____

13. rock _
    m _ _ nt _ _ ns   _____

14. un _ vers _ ty of
    fl _ r _ da   _____

15. *the s _ _ rl _ _
    letter*   _____

● WORD GAME 18

The words from the Study List are used in this puzzle. The numbers of the clues match the numbers in the puzzle. Read the clues below. Then write your answers in the puzzle blocks.

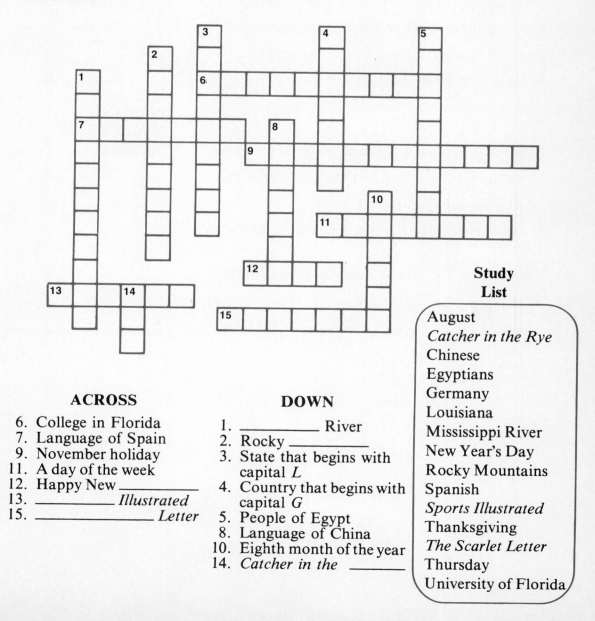

Study List

August
Catcher in the Rye
Chinese
Egyptians
Germany
Louisiana
Mississippi River
New Year's Day
Rocky Mountains
Spanish
Sports Illustrated
Thanksgiving
The Scarlet Letter
Thursday
University of Florida

ACROSS
6. College in Florida
7. Language of Spain
9. November holiday
11. A day of the week
12. Happy New _____
13. _____ *Illustrated*
15. _____ *Letter*

DOWN
1. _____ River
2. Rocky _____
3. State that begins with capital *L*
4. Country that begins with capital *G*
5. People of Egypt
8. Language of China
10. Eighth month of the year
14. *Catcher in the* _____

● HOW WELL CAN YOU SPELL?

Try to take this practice test without looking back at Lesson 18. After you have finished, check your work against the Study List. Correct any mistakes you have made.

In each of the following sentences, one word is spelled incorrectly. Find that word. Then spell it correctly on the line provided. Remember that a word is misspelled if it is not capitalized when it should be.

1. The students at the university of florada have pet alligators. _____

2. Please buy a copy of Hawthorne's *the scarlit letter.* _____

3. This flight will travel over the rockie mountains. _____

4. thankgiving is celebrated at the end of November. _____

5. The swamps of lousiana are thick with gators. _____

6. Next year we will learn how to speak spaniesh. _____

7. January first is new yeer's day. _____

8. That book has been translated from chinese into English. _____

9. Many of those automobiles are made in germiny. _____

10. The pyramids were built by the ancient egiptians. _____

11. agust is the eighth month of the year. _____

12. We will be riding the riverboat down the mississipi river. _____

13. The party will be held on thersday of next week. _____

14. The prize is a two-year subscription to *sports illestrated.*_____

15. The book report on *cacher in the rye* is due tomorrow. _____

19 Current Electricity

Think of a huge turbine engine that is larger than a sports arena. (A turbine engine is one that generates electricity.) At the center of the turbine are two large fans. Suppose that some of these turbines were sunk into the Gulf Stream off the Florida coast. The current of the stream turns the giant fans. The turbines convert the ocean's energy into electricity. The result is enough electric power to meet the needs of the State of Florida.

The plan may sound crazy. But it is one of more than 5,000 new energy ideas for the future. Scientists have fed all the information they know about the turbines into a computer. The computer gave the project a "yes" vote. But it will probably take 20 billion dollars to make the dream come true.

The turbines would be placed 25 miles (40 kilometers) off the coast of Florida. Two hundred and fifty of them would be anchored in the area called the Gulf Stream, which is the swiftest flowing ocean current in the world. Each machine would be 75 feet (22 meters) below the surface of the water. That would be deep enough so that ships in the vicinity could pass without any problem.

Scientists worry about the effect that the turbines would have on the Gulf Stream itself. The stream's current controls the weather pattern for much of the Atlantic Ocean. A change in this weather pattern might upset the environment.

In any case, scientists are looking for new ways to produce clean, cheap energy in large amounts. This must be done before our supply of oil and natural gas runs out. Ocean turbines may be one of the ways in which they will solve this problem.

● REVIEWING YOUR READING

Circle the letter beside the word or phrase that best completes the sentence.

1. A turbine engine generates

   a. water.
   b. electricity.
   c. oil.
   d. natural gas.

2. The ocean turbines may be sunk in the

   a. Gulf Stream.
   b. Pacific Ocean.
   c. Indian Ocean.
   d. Boston Harbor.

3. The turbines would generate enough electricity to supply the needs of

   a. Georgia.
   b. Alabama.
   c. Texas.
   d. Florida.

4. The Gulf Stream's current is very

   a. fast.
   b. slow.
   c. warm.
   d. cold.

5. If the turbines are used, there will be

   a. 250 of them.
   b. 500 of them.
   c. 750 of them.
   d. 1000 of them.

6. The Gulf Stream's current controls the weather pattern for much of the

   a. northwest states.
   b. southwest states.
   c. Atlantic Ocean.
   d. Pacific Ocean.

7. According to the story, you can conclude that ocean turbines

   a. are being used today.
   b. have been used for many years.
   c. are an idea for the future.
   d. will never be used.

8. According to the story, you can conclude that the ocean turbines

   a. may be one idea to help solve our energy problems.
   b. definitely will not work.
   c. are the answer to all our energy problems.
   d. are guaranteed to work.

● FIGURING THE FACTS

Decide whether the following statements are true or false. Write **T** on the line if the statement is true. If the statement is false, change the statement to make it true. Cross out the incorrect word or phrase in the sentence. Then, if necessary, write the correct word or phrase on the line.

1. At the center of the ocean there are six turbine fans. _____

2. The Gulf Stream is off the Florida coast. _____

3. The turbines will convert the ocean's energy to gasoline. _____

4. Scientists are studying more than 5,000 energy ideas. _____

5. The computer gave the turbine project a "no" vote. _____

6. The ocean turbine project will cost 100 billion dollars. _____

7. The turbines would be placed above the surface of the water. _____

8. The Gulf Stream controls the weather pattern for much of the Atlantic Ocean. _____

9. A change in the weather pattern could upset the environment. _____

10. Scientists have found many ways to produce clean, cheap energy. _____

● WHAT'S YOUR OPINION?

1. Does the idea of ocean turbines sound farfetched to you? Why or why not?

_____

_____

_____

_____

2. Why do you think we need large amounts of clean, cheap energy?

_____

_____

_____

_____

● DEVELOPING SPELLING SKILLS

**Study
List**

campaign
guarantee
impossible
merchandise
occasion
parallel
previous
probably
responsibility
thoroughly
tomorrow
tremendous
unnecessary
unusual
vicinity

The following words appear in the reading selection.

tomorrow   probably   vicinity

Because these words are more tricky to spell than other words, we call them spelling demons. Experts have found that these are words people most often misspell. However, these demons are not really difficult to spell, if we remember what it is that makes each word tricky.

Examples: In the word *tomorrow,* there is a double *r* and a *w* at the end.

In *probably,* there are two *b's.*

In *vicinity,* the "viss" sound is spelled *vic.*

Of course, you may think there are other tricky letters in these words. The most important thing for you to do is make a note of what it is that makes the word difficult for you to spell.

On your left is a Study List of words. Each is considered a spelling demon. Keep in mind that these words are ones that you will use often in your writing. Study them extra carefully. Be sure to take notice of the letters in the word that make that word difficult for you to spell.

● SKILL DRILL 1

Rewrite the following words on the lines provided. Then circle the letter or letters that make each word difficult to spell.

1. probably   _____   8. vicinity   _____

2. responsibility   _____   9. previous   _____

3. occasion   _____   10. unusual   _____

4. campaign   _____   11. unnecessary   _____

5. tomorrow   _____   12. tremendous   _____

6. guarantee   _____   13. impossible   _____

7. merchandise   _____   14. parallel   _____

15. thoroughly   _____

● SKILL DRILL 2

The following are short definitions of words from the Study List. Fill the blanks with words from the Study List that match the definitions. If you need help, check the Mini-Dictionary in the back of this book.

1. Goods for sale   _____

2. At the same distance apart everywhere   _____

3. More likely than not   _____

4. Completely; totally   _____

5. A region near or about a place   _____

6. Duty; dependability   _____

7. The day after today   _____

8. A particular time or special event   _____

9. Out of the ordinary; not usual   _____

10. A planned course of action for a special purpose (like an election)   _____

11. Not needed; not absolutely necessary   _____

12. Coming or going before; earlier   _____

13. Very great; enormous   _____

14. A promise to pay or do something if another fails   _____

15. That which cannot be done   _____

● SKILL DRILL 3

Fill the blanks in each of the following words to form words from the Study List. Then write the word you have formed on the line provided.

1. un _ _ c _ _ _ ary _____
2. un _ _ _ _ l _____
3. tom _ _ _ ow _____
4. g _ _ r _ nt _ _ _____
5. par _ _ _ el _____
6. pro _ a _ _ _ _____
7. v _ _ _ nity _____

8. pre _ _ _ us _____
9. cam _ _ _ gn _____
10. tr _ men _ _ _ s _____
11. imp _ _ _ _ ble _____
12. merch _ _ di _ _ _____
13. th _ r _ ugh _ _ _____
14. re _ _ on _ _ bility _____

15. o _ _ as _ _ n   _____

● SKILL DRILL 4

Answer the following questions by using words from the Study List.

Which words end with the suffix *ty*?

1. _____   2. _____

Which words end with the suffix *ous*?

3. _____   4. _____

Which word contains the word *rough*?

5. _____

Which words contain the letter combination *ss*?

6. _____   7. _____

Which word contains the letter combination *cc*?

8. _____

Which word contains the word *camp*?

9. _____

Which word contains the word *usual*?

10. _____

Which word contains the letter combination *ll*?

11. _____

Which word contains the prefix *pro*?

12. _____

Which word contains the word *tee*?

13. _____

Which word contains the letter combination *ise*?

14. _____

Which word contains the letter combination *rr*?

15. _____

● **WORD GAME 19**

All of the letters from the words in the Study List appear in this puzzle. Cross out the letters of the puzzle as you use them to spell the Study List words. There will be enough letters left to answer the question below.

Study List

campaign
guarantee
impossible
merchandise
occasion
parallel
previous
probably
responsibility
thoroughly
tomorrow
tremendous
unnecessary
unusual
vicinity

What are scientists looking for? _____

●HOW WELL CAN YOU SPELL?

Try to take this practice test without looking back at Lesson 19. After you have finished, check your work against the Study List. Correct any mistakes you have made.

A. One word in each of the following pairs of words is spelled incorrectly. Circle that word and spell it correctly on the line provided.

1. visinity, responsibility _____

2. tremendus, previous _____

3. impossible, throughly _____

4. campaign, unnecesary _____

5. unusual, occassion _____

6. parrallel, merchandise _____

7. probally, tomorrow _____

8. thoroughly, garuntee _____

B. In each of the following sentences, one word is spelled incorrectly. Find that word. Then spell it correctly on the line provided.

9. This puzzle seems almost imposible to do. _____

10. This campane is the most exciting one I have seen. _____

11. That was a most unuseual movie. _____

12. All of the merchandice on that table is for sale. _____

13. The test will be held the day after tomorow. _____

14. Having a family is a huge responsability. _____

15. The answer may be found in the preveus chapter. _____

20 The Haunted Jewel

For over three hundred years, the mysterious Hope Diamond has been the subject of rumor and superstition. The blue stone is one of the largest, most beautiful diamonds in the world. Legend has it that it holds the curse of a Hindu goddess.

The tale of the stone begins in India, where it once adorned the statue of a goddess. When the gem was stolen, the goddess became angry. She cursed the thieves and anyone who chose to possess the glittering jewel.

Years later in the 1700s, the gem found its way into the hands of the French queen, Marie Antoinette. However, she did not own the stone for very long. The curse plainly had its effect on Marie Antoinette, for she was beheaded during the French Revolution. Thieves then made off with the diamond, which the French people had named "the French Blue."

In 1830, the stone reappeared in London. A banker named Henry Hope purchased it for $90,000. Although Mr. Hope gave the diamond his name, the curse still seemed to be working. Henry Hope died penniless. But the diamond moved on to new owners. A European prince bought it for an actress, and later shot her. A Greek owner died with his family when his automobile went over a cliff. And a Turkish sultan who owned the stone for a few months was overthrown by his army.

The Hope's first American owner was Evelyn Walsh McLean. She had seen the diamond when it belonged to the sultan, and wished to have it. She paid twice what the stone had cost Mr. Hope—$180,000. Not fearing the curse, Mrs. McLean had the stone set into a necklace. She wore it often and with great pride. Both of her children died tragic deaths. Her husband died of mental illness.

Is it a curse or a coincidence? That depends on what you choose to believe. After Mrs. McLean's death, the stone was donated to the Smithsonian Institution in Washington, D.C. The Museum has owned the steel-blue diamond for over 20 years. No disasters have happened—yet!

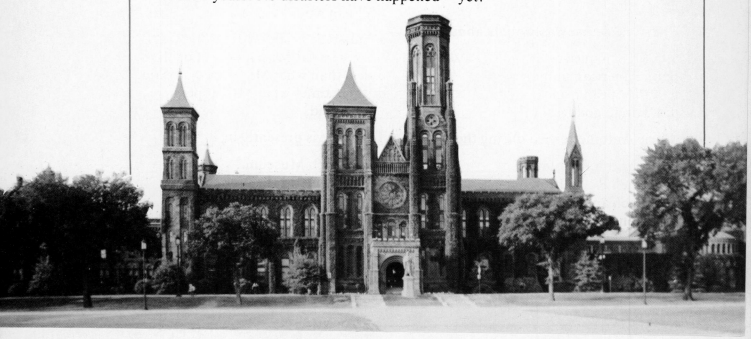

privilege [*PRIV-uh-lij*] a special right or advantage

probably [*PROB-uh-blee*] more likely than not

proceed [*pruh-SEED*] to move forward

proclaim [*proh-KLAYM*] to declare or make known publicly

punctuation [*pungk-choo-AY-shun*] the use of certain marks in written language to make the meaning clear

pursuit [*pur-SOOT*] the act of pursuing or following

R

radio [*RAY-dee-oh*] a way of sending or receiving sounds by electric waves
Plural: **radios** [*RAY-dee-ohs*]

radish [*RAD-ish*] a small, crisp red vegetable
Plural: **radishes** [*RAD-ish-es*]

rapidly [*RAP-id-lee*] very swiftly or quickly

realize [*REE-uh-lyz*] to understand clearly

really [*REE-uh-lee*] truly or actually

recently [*REE-sunt-lee*] happening a short time ago

recommend [*rek-uh-MEND*] to speak in favor of or advise

recruit [*rih-KROOT*] to get new members

reference [*REF-ur-uns*] the act of referring or consulting

reflex [*REE-fleks*] an automatic response
Plural: **reflexes** [*REE-fleks-ez*]

relaying [*REE-lay-ing*] taking something and carrying it farther

reliable [*rih-LY-uh-bul*] dependable; worthy of trust

relying [*rih-LY-ing*] depending on or trusting

remembrance [rih-MEM-bruns] the act of remembering

respectfully [*rih-SPEKT-ful-lee*] feeling or showing respect

responsibility [*rih-spon-suh-BIL-ih-tee*] duty; dependability

revise [*rih-VYZ*] to make corrections or improvements

ring [*RING*] to make a clear sound by touching or striking

rodeo [*ROH-dee-oh*] a contest in riding horses or roping cattle
Plural: **rodeos** [*ROH-dee-ohs*]

rumor [*ROO-mur*] a story or statement lacking in proof or truth

S

salvage [*SAL-vij*] to rescue or save from being thrown away

sandwich [*SAND-wich*] two slices of bread with filling between such as meat or cheese
Plural **sandwiches** [*SAND-wich-es*]

satisfied [*SAT-is-fyd*] contented or fulfilled

scene [*SEEN*] the time or place of a play, story, or happening

schedule [*SKEJ-ool*] written or printed statement of details
Plural: **schedules** [*SKEJ-ools*]

sealing [*SEEL-ing*] closing tightly

secretary [*SEK-rih-ter-ee*] skilled office worker

seen [*SEEN*] having looked at

separate [*SEP-uh-rayt*] to keep apart; divide

separately [*SEP-ur-it-lee*] divided into parts or groups; individually

September [*sep-TEM-bur*] the ninth month of the year

serious [*SEER-ee-us*] important; grave

shampoo [*sham-POO*] a soap used to wash hair
Plural: **shampoos** [*sham-POOZ*]

shelf [*SHELF*] a piece of wood that is fastened to a wall to hold things such as books
Plural: **shelves** [*SHELVZ*]

sheriff [*SHER-if*] a law enforcement officer
Plural: **sheriffs** [*SHER-ifs*]

shouldn't [*SHOOD-unt*] should not

sketch [*SKECH*] a rough or quickly done drawing
Plural: **sketches** [*SKECH-es*]

soprano [*suh-PRAN-oh*] a singer with the highest singing voice there is
Plural: **sopranos** [*suh-PRAN-ohs*]

spectator [*SPEK-tay-tur*] a person who watches an event
Plural: **spectators** [*SPEK-tay-turz*]

speeches [*SPEECH-es*] public talks

splice [*SPLYS*] to join together

standardize [*STAN-dur-dyz*] to make standard in size, weight, shape, etc.

statue [*STACH-oo*] an image carved in stone, wood, etc.

stereo [*STER-ee-oh*] a record player or radio that brings sound from two directions
Plural: **stereos** [*STER-ee-ohs*]

stitch [*STICH*] a loop of thread made while sewing
Plural: **stitches** [*STICH-es*]

straighten [*STRAYT-un*] to make straight

strayed [*STRAYD*] wandered or roamed away

studio [*STOO-dee-oh*] a workroom for a painter or other artist
Plural: **studios** [*STOO-dee-ohs*]

study [*STUD-ee*] a lesson or school subject
Plural: **studies** [*STUD-eez*]

succeed [*suk-SEED*] to turn out well; to have success

summarize [*SUM-uh-ryz*] to make a summary of

superior [*suh-PEER-ee-ur*] very good or above average

supplied [*suh-PLYD*] having satisfied a need or provided a quantity of something

surveying [*sur-VAY-ing*] looking over or viewing something; skimming

swaying [*SWAY-ing*] swinging back and forth

T

theater [*THEE-uh-tur*] a place where plays are acted

thief [*THEEF*] one who steals
Plural: **thieves** [*THEEVS*]

thoroughly [*THUR-oh-lee*] completely; totally

Thursday [*THURZ-dee*] the fifth day of the week

tomato [*tuh-MAY-toh*] a juicy, red vegetable
Plural: **tomatoes** [*tuh-MAY-tohs*]

tomorrow [*tuh-MOR-oh*] the day after today

tornado [*tor-NAY-doh*] a violent and destructive storm; a whirlwind
Plural: **tornadoes** [*tor-NAY-dohs*]

totally [*TOHT-uh-lee*] completely; entirely; in a total manner

tremendous [*trih-MEN-dus*] very great; enormous

trophy [*TROH-fee*] a prize for the winner of a contest
Plural: **trophies** [*TROH-feez*]

Tuesday [*TOOZ-dee*] the third day of the week

U

understood [*un-dur-STOOD*] to have learned the meaning of something

unnecessary [*un-NES-ih-ser-ee*] not needed; not absolutely necessary

unusual [*un-YOO-zhoo-ul*] out of the ordinary; not usual

V

vacuum [*VAK-yoo-um*] an empty space without any air in it

valley [*VAL-ee*] low land between hills or mountains
Plural: **valleys** [*VAL-leez*]

valuable [*VAL-yoo-uh-bul*] having value;

vegetable [*VEJ-tuh-bul*] a plant used for food

vicinity [*vih-SIN-ih-tee*] a region near or about a place

vitamin [*VY-tuh-min*] special substances needed for the nourishment of the body

volcano [*vol-KAY-noh*] a mountain that expels steam and lava
Plural: **volcanoes** [*vol-KAY-nohz*]

W

wearily [*WEER-uh-lee*] in a tired or worn-out way

weather [*WETH-ur*] climate conditions

Wednesday [*WENZ-dee*] the fourth day of the week

we'll [*WEEL*] we will

wharf [*HWORF*] a platform for loading and unloading ships
Plural: **wharves** [*HWORVZ*]

where's [*HWAIRZ*] where is

whether [*HWETH-ur*] if

wife [*WYF*] a married woman
Plural: **wives** [*WYFZ*]

wish [*WISH*] an expression of a desire or want
Plural: **wishes** [*WISH-es*]

wolf [*WOOLF*] a wild animal somewhat like a dog
Plural: **wolves** [*WOOLVZ*]

woman [*WOOM-un*] an adult female human
Plural: **women** [*WIM-in*]

won't [*WOHNT*] will not

wouldn't [*WOOD-unt*] would not

wrap [*RAP*] to cover with paper and string

wreckage [*REK-ij*] the remains of something ruined

wring [*RING*] to squeeze or twist

Y

yourself [*yoor-SELF*] you
Plural: **yourselves** [*yoor-SELVZ*]

you've [*YOOV*] you have